SUITC

HAIR

A journey into the Afro & Asian Experience

Poems and stories by UK writers of colour

HAIR

ISBN 1-905778-01-5

Acknowledgements

'Ombre' by John Siddique from *The Prize* (Rialto 2005)

Ghazal Couplets introduction from Debjani Chatterjee's Introduction to *Generations of Ghazals* (Redbeck Press 2003)

'The Hot Comb', by Cheryl Martin Previously published in *AFTERSHOCK*, Commonwealth Games 2002. From an Exhibit in Moving Lives, Pump House Museum April 2002

'The Last Time' by Anjum Malik from *Before The Rains* (University Press, Huddersfield 1995)

'The Shave' by SuAndi from *There Will Be No Tears* (The Pankhurst Press 1995)

'Close Shave' by Jackie Kay from *The Adoption Papers* (Bloodaxe Books, 1991)

'At Antoine's Barber Shop' by John Lyons from *the sun rises in the north* (Smith/Doorstop Books 1991)

'Hair' by Debjani Chatterjee from *I Was That Woman* (Hippopotamus Press, 1989)

First published in 2006 by Suitcase

Suitcase books are published by
Shorelines @
Commonword Ltd
6 Mount Street
Manchester M2 5NS
www.shorelines.org.uk
info@shorelines.org.uk

Shorelines gratefully acknowledges financial assistance from the Arts Council of England and Manchester City Council

Suitcase books are distributed by Turnaround Publisher Services Ltd, Unit 3, Olympia Trading Estate, Coburg Rd, Wood Green, London N22 6TZ.

Cover design by Ian Bobb (07799137492)
Cover photograph by Semonara Chowdhry

Printed by LPPS Ltd, 128 Northampton Rd, Wellingborough, NN8 3PJ

British Library Cataloguing-in-Publication Data. A catalogue record for this book is available from the British Library.

Contents

The Salon & The Barber Shop

Irie

Love, Solitude

Seniors

Myth, Mystery

Childhood & Children's Poems

Ghazal Couplets

Short Stories

Problem Pages with Khadija Rehman

Styling Tips with Shirley May & Pete Kalu

Alternatively, for a laugh....

Introduction

Introduction

To see the world in a grain of sand

'How does my hair look?' Anyone who has been flummoxed by this simple question will know how intriguing hair can be. It is both the simple stuff that grows out of our head, and a maze of meanings, references and pointers. For all cultures, the way in which hair is worn can denote orthodoxy and conformity, rebellion and difference; it can show the mood of an individual, and the zeitgeist of the times.

In the harsh, knuckle-down climate of the 50's in the UK, newly arrived émigrés of the West Indies sometimes straightened their hair using hot combs, not only for convenience, but in an attempt to conform to white notions of beauty.

Then, in the Sixties came a new, emancipatory energy, in tune with the burgeoning black consciousness movement. There was a celebratory embracing of natural hair, which reached its zenith in the adoption of big Afros as people of African origin celebrated their difference and pride in African heritage.

Black is beautiful

Within Asian communities the presentation of hair has also had strong cultural resonances. Hair can denote wisdom, religious zeal, beauty, sexuality. More recently the question of covering or uncovering hair for Muslims in an increasingly Islamophobic society has held important messages – political and religious.

It is not just the way hair is tied or worn, but the actual process of tying and plaiting that can also hold significance – the memories of tying and combing can express family power structures and frustrations as well as moments of love and bonding.

There is now a very twenty-first century plethora of styles seen on the streets and in houses: natural, loose, covered, tied, locked, plaited, weaved, treated, dyed; even wigs have made something of a comeback. Many African hair styles have become mainstream, with young black girls corn-rowing their white friends' hair and white men and women sporting locks, plaits and extensions.

This book chronicles it all. From bad hair days to wedding days, from those dishevelled moments of intimacy to the conscious cultivation of locks as a political act; from the shaving of the head as an act of rebellion and resistance, to the tantalising perfume released by long hair.

Hair Raisin

When we put out the call for submissions, the response came overwhelmingly from women. This suggests that the social, cultural, aesthetic and political significance of hair and its appearance is stronger for women than men.

The contributors' backgrounds are wide ranging: from office workers and landladies to teachers and plumbers, from teenagers to poets in their Eighties. The only criterion has been that the poems must move and engage, tell something new, or reveal something old in a fresh light.

As we read the texts, natural groupings suggested themselves. These became the sections of the collection and they should be understood as loose guide posts. Several poems could have sat easily in more than one section, and some seemed not completely at home in any.

Frizzical

The forms adopted by the contributors are wide-ranging: short alliterative poems, long epic poems, Japanese influenced haiku-like pieces, Asian lyrical ghazals, as well as short stories and texts that hover somewhere between poetry and prose. We have also included humorous and/or profound quotations on hair from around the world, an Agony Aunt section, and a short section on styling hair that is both practical and (occasionally) tongue in cheek!

We hope you will find the collection engaging, challenging and uplifting. All errors are ours alone. We would like to thank editorial consultants, Khadijah Ibrahiim and Qaisra Shahraz; and advisors, Anandi Ramamurthy, Kadija George and Tariq Mehmood.

The Editors, Pete Kalu, Shirley May

At Mama's Feet

Third Word Language

Eileen Pun

Hello, hello, hello, he said
One for my breasts, face and breasts again.
I went with him because I liked him,
He knew my mother's third word language.

I learned it while she was on the telephone,
With my hair in her hand and ears between knees,
Sitting underneath the black comb.

Talking to my godmother, or maybe my aunt,
But mostly to the lady from the market
Who said – excoose me this, or excoose me that,
About the minister's daughter pregnant at seventeen.

Shame. Shame. Shame, my mother would have sighed,
Then tugged at my unruly hair with her powerful
straight comb.
Inside my tender head I am a much greater size –
just wait till I get old.
Only in *this* country, she says. When they can vote,
they think they is grown.

Are grown. But if I corrected her,
Or put my hand where it throbbed,
She would slap my fingers with the black handle.
What did I say? Must I tell you the same thing
every single day?

But I remember –
Things she said only once, or when she was soft spoken.
My feet were like my father's,
There was bad news from an itching palm,
A woman was only a girl a man had broken.

Enough, enough, enough, he said.
Listening to me sob;
About the knots in my hair,
About nothing in particular,
About turning my back on God.

The comb was much too heavy in the cradle of her skirt,
It made tight folds against her thigh.
So how could I tell her, about the growth inside my
womb?
About how he could lie, lie, lie.

At once she hugged me, longer than I've ever known.
Sounded like so much understanding when she said,
My, my, my.

Next

Shirley May

She held me gripped between her legs, I leaned
into the familiar smell of freshly chopped

thyme, curry, seasonall and raw meat
still lingering on her clothes and hands

mama's wash belly was first, the youngest
and luckiest of five girls. she turned my head

as though it was a mechanism separate
from my neck and shoulders. I jerked back

she manoeuvred me in her vice like grip
between her large thighs and began to part my hair.

I hummed familiar tunes, echoes between each ouch
and why are you pulling so hard

her reply incoherent, laced with *rasss*
and another *Jesus is my saviour*, as she combed

through knots and then brushed I often wondered
why she did not brush then comb

(my own daughter asked me that question)
turn to me, she said. The best position to be in

closest to her smell. You could cradle
your head in her lap, tended with love and hate

both at the same time. She called out
to the second to last child for the white ribbon.

two huge bows either side of my head
she shouted *Finished. Next.*

The Hot Comb

Cheryl Martin

Inside the museum case it looks innocent.
'Iron straightening-comb'.
An artefact,
Elevated by the chill glass,
The precise academic label.

But I know the damn truth.
Every Saturday
Mama washing my hair
Pulling at the naps
Till I scream

(I'm tenderheaded.
Nobody can touch my head
But me.)

Watch the comb
Heat up on top of the stove
Till the devil-thing turns red
Just like the priest promised:
Red-hot torture
For all my sins.
(Yelling at my little sister,
Sitting on my brother's back
And trying to break it
For no reason.
No reason.)

Play statue
While it sizzles in my still-wet hair,
Pray it doesn't burn my ear.
(It's embarrassing to go to school
With comb-marks on your neck.)

Pretend I don't smell
That scorch-stink.
Hope it doesn't rain
Soon as I walk out the door
So it all goes right back to nappy.
See how my long straight hair
Makes my mother happy.

Plaits

Tanya Chan Sam

My grandmother stands at the edges of my thoughts,
calling me back. Plaits my hair into tight braids,
which pull, sharp, at the edges of my face.

Her comb, brush and oil tempers my voskop,
clenched scissors chomp nests of gum and tangles.
My head parts into parallel universes.

She combs from my eyebrows up. My neck elongates,
my eyes turn corners to follow the rutted route of
    tooth combs.
Large knuckles silence the screams on my stinging scalp.

She bevels my curls with oiled palms, plaits and weaves
my childhood into red ribbons, rubber bands and
    taut tears,
tends each pigtail until it reaches my knees.

She oils her disappointments into my wiry fringe,
rubs the last drops of olive oil into my moonface cheeks.
Calling me back, from the edges of my thoughts.

***Voskop** – untidy head of hair*

Mother-Daughter

Sitara Khan

Enveloped in a thick blanket of dark hair
scalp stinging, tears rolling,
clamped between her feet,
between my mother's legs I sit.

Her dainty hands oiled, combed and disentangled
their way through the unruly mass.

Weighed by tradition I struggled to free myself,
of bob cut and hair dressers' salons I dared to dream.

School mates' envy brought little relief.
My mother's instinct whispered in my ear:
'Mother's loving milk has nurtured your hair.
In its lustrous length is woven the yarn
from ancestral antiquity to who you now are.
With this dowry I do thee trust
which for other cares you must not neglect.'

The bonding tie between mother and daughter was such
that scissors of rebellion could never touch.

Getting it Right

Jolivia Gaston

VO5 shampoo or supermarket special
Which one will she choose?
My Afro curls diluted in water
'I can't get the soap out'
Mother cried
The soap still anchored to my scalp
Half an hour later I stood motionless
Water cascading down my neck
Inside my ears
I felt a towel round my head
Mum's finished
The hair dryer on full heat
Made my hair brittle
Like a Brillo-Pad
I look in the mirror
The reflection stares at me
I shut my eyes
Mum said 'you're too emotional.
Use this', she announced.
Placing the Bryl-Creem
Inside my hand
When I look back I wonder
If my father ever noticed
His Bryl-Creem shrinking
Years later Afro/Sheen replaced Bryl-Creem
The Jerry/Curl replaced Afro/Curls
And braided hair replaced straight hair
Whenever we talk about

Bad Hair Days
Mum and I start laughing
She could never get it right

Daughter

Elaine Okoro

When you grew inside me
I worried you be a girl
Whose hair I couldn't plait
Lost skills not passed from mother to daughter
Memories of hot comb were not what I wanted for you.

I self-taught on plastic dolls
So you could have a natural beauty
In corn-row, coloured bobbles and slides

And as a teenager
You bought into Black identity
As what you wore,
What your hair looked liked.
Ironically you straightened and preened your hair,
As it was more manageable!

One day a hairdresser cut off your hair.
You wanted to run into your mother's arms
And hide.

I told you your hair doesn't make you any less
Beautiful or Black than you are,
Hair is a journey and a passage to who you were then
And who you are now.
Like you.... hair grows.

Retreat

Kanta Walker

In the tangle
Of her long dark hair
Covering the curves
Of her little child
Buttocks – I hid
My desires

The corkscrew curls
That lined her
Angelic face
And exaggerated
The innocence
Of her coal black eyes
Shook defiantly and said
'Old woman, I am
Taking your young love
Away – on a joy-ride!'

Oh, the caprice
Of the shake of her
Shoulders! Denying
Me confidence,
Shouting, retreat, retreat, RETREAT!

Should I have brought
My age-old charms out?
Used my guile and wit
To keep myself warm

In bed a bit longer?

No! I wanted her to win
And dance all night
Away in a dim lit
Dance-hall and hold
My lover in her arms
And spin, and spin,
AND SPIN!

The Mirror

Kanta Walker

A young girl
closely observes her
hot chestnut curls
streaked with red and gold
rearranges the waves;
the shimmering opulence
sings and kisses her sinuous hips.

Some half a century on
a rotund figure wearing black
looks back with sad eyes:
yesterday's young loves
flew off or became round
shouldered and fat bellied

An infant's smile of recognition
takes her back in time;
a young girl will naturally
look at herself in the mirror
ready to rewrite history.

Strewth!

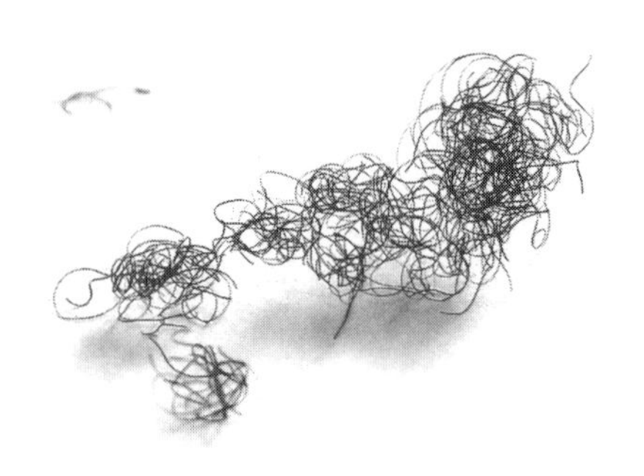

Wiggy

Chanje Kunda

Worthy women wearing wraps
Wonder whether we worship
Whites when we wear weaves
When we're wonderful without
Wonder why we wantonly
wage war on wild woolly
wondrous weightlessness

7 millisecond itch

Shamshad Khan

It's a good hair day.
long hair
loose
scrunch dried
I'm out

in company

dinner for six.

when I get that seven millisecond itch
so quick

but there's no mistaking it

that pin prick
at the nape of the neck

before they serve the starters
I think
back.

a week ago
rubbing heads with
my nieces under sixes
primary school carriers
of colds, sneezes

and jeeze
there it goes again
behind my ears.
I try not to
but it's relentless
a casual scratch

is not enough.

we've just started the first course
and my whole scalp is creeping
bloodthirsty dinner guests
coming back for seconds

I'm scratching non -stop and scheming
broad day light.
one bottle of conditioner.
and a very fine toothed comb
my weapons of choice

Personal Profile

Chanje Kunda

Name : Chakwa Mwape Lwimbo
Date of birth : Post slavery
Post colonialism
Place of birth : Wrong place for
Money, health or
Prosperity
Nationality : Alien
Colour of hair : Not long blonde
Does not sway
In the breeze
According to L'Oreal
I'm not worth it
Colour of eyes : Not like deep
Blue pools
Colour of skin : Not like Irish cream
Cheeks don't glow
Like an English rose
Height : As small as
You wish
To make me
Feel
Build : Not Big breasted
Not long legged
Not sexy slender
Not pert buttocked
Occupation : 21st Century
Girl/ woman
Person

HAIR

Elayne Ogbeta

H aveityourway
A nystyleyouwant
I nseasonoutofseason
R eflectionofyourself

home (road to Ilorin)

Segun Lee-French

red earth
green bush
grey tarmac
hot wind
                    yr black nylon wig
in my nose

an alternative to plastination

Shamshad Khan

each ant
will carry one single black hair
each

eyebrow
eye lash
nose bristle

moustache
goatee whisker
bum fluff
pubic hair
big toe tuft

then there will be a ceremonial line dance
as the ants

following a detailed body map
build
a hair and air effigy

replica
of you

and if we were still in love

I would arrange
to have a few stray hairs
of mine

woven in between the spaces
that would be you

Bill

Aissatou Sylla

Detangling shampoo, £6
Anti-Freeze Conditioner, £5
Gel, £4
Relaxing pack, £6
Fortnightly hairdresser, £30
Moisturisers, £20
Placenta capsules, olive oil, cocoa butter, shea butt…
Aaaahhh!!!!!

Pass me that wig!
Gotta feed the kids.

a really neat cleaning tip that can double up as a treatment for alopecia
(patent Sunara Begum Khan)

Shamshad Khan

you will need:

one damp cloth
a bowl of warm water
a few drops of Dettol to get an extra fresh finish

whether it's you
or the dog
who's moulting

the following technique is great for removing
the film of hair that coats
your carpet or any other fabric

instructions:

get down on your knees
take the damp cloth
squeeze out excess water into the bowl
with the damp cloth wipe the surface of the carpet
use firm sweeping actions
drawing the loose hair towards you

if you have suffered extreme hair loss
hair recovered in this way can be used to create a weave
or natural looking toupee

for best effects:
rinse cloth and repeat

Black Hair Day

Julian Daniel

You could stroll through Shrewsbury,
With your dangly bits for all to see.

Or attend a church meeting at the local vicar's,
With your skirt riding up your knickers.

And no matter how absurd,
No one will utter a word.

But

As soon as you're having a bad hair day,
Every Tom, Dick and Kwame's got something to say.

Black Triangle

John Lyons

It hovered above my head, a black patch
bristling like a dog-scared cat.

Even when a hand came down, scratched it
in the small-window twilight
of the room, it remained silent.

I wanted to reach out and touch it,
but something held me back.

I knew it from somewhere,
that mouth stretched to the limit
and my being forced out
into the blinding light, deafening noise
once echoes filtered through water.

I lived again the musk
of closeness, the touch
of a body-warmed chemise,
a nuzzling softness
and sweetness in my throat
to stop me crying.

The Salon & The Barber Shop

At Antoine's Barber Shop

John Lyons

There was a time, swivelled to its full height,
I still needed a wooden box in the barber's chair.

I was growing to the decreasing swivel of a man:
'If only yuh dead mudder could see you now,'
Antoine said.

I listened to the rapid scissor talk and barber shop debate:
'Man, Sugar Ray could box fuh so!
He better than your Joe Louis, any day.
I telling yuh, HE was a sweet sweet mover.
Joe Louis flat-footed, cahn dance like ole Sugar.'

And when the razor came out unfolded,
slapping itself keen on the leather strap,
I held my breath, stopped listening
till soap suds were wiped away.

'Brilliantined', talc-powdered,
unscathed with short back and sides,
I left the barber shop shadow boxing.

hair salon (osogbo)

Segun Lee French

fuji drums
attack the air with beaten tongues of copper.
The electric wind,
my ears shiver
& speakers struggle to survive.

They punch,
they pound,
they warp
the sound
of hand & skin.
They bully
the air
till she sings,

lai lai mo ni fe e
lai lai mo ni fe e

Hair
twists
at
my feet.

Mosquitoes
taste my bitter
potion
& scatter.

Yr head is caked
in burning
foam.

it's for u i do this
u say u no like my wig

& so,
this sweaty room,
yellow bulb,
f l i c k e r i n g
fan,
trailing dust
sta sta sta
lag lag lag
tit tit tit
e e e
s s s
. . .

The sweet factory smell
as burning flowers flutter
from an aerosol
can.

fuji drums
beat
the air into submission.
The static makes each hair gyrate.
Speakers vibrate so fast
they have no shape.

They batter,
they bash,
they blur
the sound becomes a brutal mash.

They torture the air
till she sings,

lai lai mo ni fe e
lai lai mo ni fe e

Back to back,
2 hairdressers
tweak
2 heads
of hardened curls
with nylon tongs,
fingers
in clear plastic sheaths.

At last, they rinse the chrysalis
away,
& u emerge,
so sleek
& shiny,
wriggling
in my embrace,
born again waves
still wet,
because...

NEPA don take the light away

No power,
no hairdryer,
no *fuji* drums.

It's dark now,
time for cricket song.
& we leave
the salon
girls,
sweeping up
nylon curls,

voices

thin

as wind.

lai lai mo ni fe e

lai lai mo ni fe e

***fuji**: Music played by Yoruba in Nigeria - voices accompanied by hand drums.*
***lai lai mo ni fe e:** (Yoruba) I will love you for ever.*
***NEPA**: Nigerian Electricity and Power Authority (otherwise known as Never Ever Power At All! due to daily power cuts)*

Permanent Damage

Tina Tamsho Thomas

My appointment was for one o'clock,
though I arrived some minutes early,
eager for to see each lock
spiralled, chic and curly.

'Sit there, madam – wear this cape,
is this the style you're wanting?
A spiral perm, the perfect shape,
it shouldn't be too daunting.'

What did she mean? I sat and mused,
the manager sauntered by,
'you're the spiral, never mind,
we can at least but try.'

A stylist came and eyed my hair
with something like dismay,
'It should turn out, but just in case
I'll get the bosses say.'

Fears and qualms now filled my mind,
'Please tell me what's the trouble?'
A talking head quite floored the man,

he bolted at the double.

A trainee told me things were fine,
then sprayed my hair with water,
soaked my clothes through to the skin,
I wondered damply who had taught her.

'It's taking shape,' the stylist beamed,
then applied the rollers,
carried away with a sharp steel comb,
I nearly lost two molars.

Then she oiled my sodden strands,
with lubricant excessive,
greasy spirals, leaden curls,
my new look looked depressive.

Hours passed - free at last
from the elastic, plastic grippers,
under the dryer my breathing eased,
till she approached me with the snippers.

'Just an inch,' she beamed once more,
'but I don't want it cutting.'
A difficult client, her eyes accused,
she went off loudly tutting.

The acrid smell of perm solution
was soon upon each tress,
my senses permeated,
such was my distress.

The end result of my processed hair,
was there for all to assess,
then I knew why they'd had their doubts,
it looked such a bloody mess!

Aunty Ida's

Yvonne McCalla

sitting
in the back room
at Aunty Ida's
the straightening comb
kissing its teeth
as it hits the grease
the acrid smell of
frying hair excites
a delicious anticipation
a Saturday night celebration
as the blue smoke rises
curling around a thousand
dreams

Irie

Big Wig n Sugar Brown

Khadijah Ibrahiim

I

Bigwig. A braggadacio fat spender
at auction block a real trend setter
A red faced man, breathing stink
sweat of rum and whisky

Kilted his way cross-seas
Groomed on Big White Wigs
of law and order, so brazen
he modelled a tangled wig of treachery
to crown lice eaten head,
with whip and overseer

He hampered truth lived words
sanctified by the hands of men
in the name of a different kind of god

II

She, a Fanti girl, Wolof, Ibo
or Mandingo, we are not sure
He called her Sugar Brown
He never knew her name

All recall her beauty
her skin the blackest of brown,
molasses-smooth,
cane juice sweet
a china bump plait head girl

not past 15
sea salt assailed
slave ship whipped
cutlass in hand, working cane fields
she sings her song

And everyone knew the words

how he used his thick red
fingers like the housemaid's broomstick, how he
pushed his way between Sugar Brown's thighs

Sweet Sugar Brown he cried
heaving his full fist
up inside, loosen pants pressed
pale pink body against hers

his wig slipped over one eye
as he dipped. Saliva dripped
from corner mouth he heightened
his pleasure

Sweet Sugar Brown, he cried,
His breath stained with highland
whisky, pork belly and stewed dumplings

He pulls on her plaits
and with breathing jolts
quickens his pace, burying flesh inside
Rubbing sweat around her breast
Spits whispers into face
Surely I've paid well for you,
Ma prize lass. I did not select in haste

Sweet Sugar Brown, he cried
Again and again, he gripped the bedpost
Gave another jolt, his wig fell
Like a dead rat onto her chest

She eyes piercing corner ceiling
Searching for home, eyes squeezed shut
To his fat balding head of
Granite grey hair stuck between
dried scabs. Puss filled bumps. Skin
Powder dust thick

He jolted franticly. Again and again
And again.
He pitched a groan
released his grip turned and pissed in a pot
shouting,

Get thee here each day and know my face by
night,
Get thee in my big house, from my cane fields,
Get thee in my bed, warm my feet,
spread at my will,
groom my wig each day,
curl my ends and bow to me.

And everyone knows the words to the song
And all knew of a Massa Bigwig

who could never own the soul
break the spirit of the plantations.

Dark Flowers

Desiree Reynolds

If I am Black, but
My hair is not, will the blood
In small flowers bright,
And dark, from Bombay and Kingston
Stop flowing down my school shirt?

Why I Became Natural

Melanie Duncan

Because it was the natural thing for me to do.

My hair didn't like to be fried every three months
It feigned baldness when I blew it out
Knowing this was my biggest fear
It made me touch it to see
That it hadn't left me
And the stress of that was too much!

So I began to plait it, twist it and kemet bump it
And it thrived and thrived
Made me realise the myth that
Black people can't have natural long hair
Was a big lie to sell perms
My hair just won't stop growing
And showing off.
Just stands there, attracting attention
Allowing itself to evolve me
And make me appreciate the beauty
Within me, leading me to love me
As I am, naturally.

Head Wraps

Rachel Van Den Bergen

I've burn' it.
Stretched it.
Curled it.
Turned it into an oil slick.

Then the hairdresser told me how to use a wrap.

So I wrapped it.
Nurtured it.
Caressed it.
Dressed it.

You can get them in many colours and shades.
When your hair is feeling crap.
You can't beat a good old traditional African wrap.
The best thing for bad hair days.

Black is

Jade Lloyd

Black

is
the
colour
of my true
loves hai R

black

is
the
texture of
his caressing

curls

black

is
the
rhythm
of hai R day

blues

black is
black is
black is

the
vibe
of
my true

hai R

black is
black is
black is

Uncut

Jade Lloyd

Mumia Abu-Jamal

re:fuses 2 cut
his long dreadlocks

re:fuses 2 cut
a peoples vocal cords

re:fuses 2 cut
All things censored

re:fuses 2 cut
so we
hai R

Hai R

Jade Lloyd

is a
good
place 2
begin as

any
singing
at me:

[fraggle rock
hai R bear bunch
kate bush
fuzzy bear
hai R sticks up like
telephone wire]

no no no…
i aint
no liar

typical:
school day

[turn her
upside
down &
use
her as a mop]

the kind ly elder ly
elders of the church?
Wob bow ow ow

wo
man

Id like
2
C u try

Truth or

Jade Lloyd

hai R
is
my

history
identity
soul 4
real

natural
wild
afro
texture

hai R
pulling
[can I touch it]

name
calling
[is it REAL]

soul
struggling
[looks like a wig]

my
hai R truth

Mother

Elaine Okoro

There is a reason I locked at forty-four
I think I am only realising now (a year on)
The link within and without
Between the seed and growth
beginning and end.

My mother passed
But photos of her with her straightened hair
Leap a generation and make me smile.
Grandmother and granddaughter alike yet never met
There is a breath of emotion
stored in the connections, in this
coiled energy of hair we share between us.

There is a reason I began to locks
And the reason keeps growing and forming
And falling in this process of life.
Each seed grows with a story to tell.

So there is a reason I started
My locks
There is a reason.

Road

Trudy Blake

Men working on the road.
Digging, digging, and singing.
Fe me boss a work house boss.
The boss would come up and
hear them.
He say don't sing that.
Sing muma me want man.

They would start singing
muma we want man
Look how me bubby a jump.
Muma me want man,
Look on the hair at me front.

When the boss leave, they
would sing
Fe me boss a work house boss.
They sing and they dig the road.

When it is near time to go home
It's a different tune then.
It goes like this.
Late oh, late oh, late \ a come.
Look upon the dummy clock,
Late a come.

Dreadlocked

Sheree Mack

Where ya come from?

Newcastle.
No really ....
Bradford?

Gonna get me hair locked,
dreadlocked

London.
Gonna get rooted, locked
dreadlocked

Brixton market
Saturday morning
passing through,
mustn't linger.

Huge purple stone
wrapped in silver
fit snug
around my finger.

Reminded me of them
poets with props
words held my attention, locked
dreadlocked.

The dreads were awesome
but the Florida heat
too long, too heavy
cut, lick, slick, gone overnight.

Nappy sore fingered hair left.
I can see my neck
I can see my face
My smile, locked,
dreadlocked.

Natural High

Jackie Simpson

Dem seh me tough, unruly, out a control.
A LIE DEM A TELL!

Watch de weave, a hang dung dem back.
Watch de relaxer, a eat out dem head back.
Watch de perm, saturated wid fat.
Dem mashin up my existence,
Wid dem chemicals and chat.

But me live like a wire,
an wi keep coming back.
Till dem bun out me roots,
Wid dem chemicals and chat.

Released

Kauser Parveen

I cut my hair
An act of revenge
An act of defiance
For me I wanted it
As I wanted it
No more conforming to
Other people's expectations
No more
Keeping up appearances
I cut it to illustrate
It was my way of taking control
It was my way of asserting power
Over a man
Who had controlled every aspect of my life
Or at least he thought he had

Adopted Child

Kauser Parveen

The products they put on my hair
The creams they put on my face
The clothes they made me wear
The food I was told to eat
The school I was made to attend
The things I was taught
All changed
All erased
All made me feel alienated
I was being anglicised
Everything about me was changed
From the first moment of independence
From the first moment of free thinking
I binned the clothes
Let my hair fly naturally
Soothed my skin with cocoa butter
Read the books of my choice
Ate all the foods of purity
I had arrived

Rising

Chanje Kunda

A skiffle
Tingly, prickly
Under my hands
A stubble
Spiky scratching
My face
My mouth

Curling hairs
Across your
chest brushes
Against my
Body
Your breath
Sounds heavy
Gasping my name
Wrapped
Around me
you are
My nest
My home
My world

I am the stars
I am the night sky
I'm dread
The strength of my roots
Keeps me pushing through
Keeps me rising up

Proud, defiant
Free

You're Blacker Than You Think

Jolivia Gaston

I

You go around thinking
You're someone else

The next thing you maintain
You're not black

Your skin is lighter
It passes the grade

Though your hair
Gives you away

Afro-curls
Long or straight

Your disguise
People see through it

II

What's in your head
No one can read

Only in solitude
You admit the truth

Inside you
Blackness is growing

The Circle

Shirley May

Her wisdom was young like her years

Driving fast, I wanted to get home
She told me to take my time.

Her speech fast, I could not keep up with her
So I breathed, short breaths then long ones

I was sure she would asphyxiate on her next line
And I'd be left telling her parents she'd been with me

I found myself breathing for her, gasping at air
As I followed, turning corners with her

All I could think was, why don't you breathe?

I had known a long time she was different
A sassiness about her, a sexiness

She stretched to feel her hair, to show a little flesh
She had grown wise like the women of her family,
knowing their secrets.

I tried a couple of times to inject an aunt's wisdom
That was not for a Circle night, a night of confession

Things she had done told to me all the way home.

How she gone change. She was full grown.

From the minute she entered The Circle Club
she loved me, until the minute I left her outside her
front door.

Stopped outside her gate, kissed her like kin should.

An ex-lover murdered that weekend
Her ex-boyfriend locked up for eighteen years.

I said something random
You ever thought bout plaiting ya hair before ya go a bed?

Love, Solitude

Close Shave

Jackie Kay

The only time I forget is down the pit
right down in the belly of it,
my lamp shining like a third eye,
my breath short and fast like my wife's
when she's knitting. Snip snap.
I've tried to tell her as many times
as I've been down this mine. I can't
bring myself to, she'd tell our girls
most probably. It doesn't bear thinking.

Last night he shaved me again.
Close. Such an act of trust.
And he cut my hair; the scissors snip
snipped all night as I lay beside Ella
(Good job she's not that interested)
I like watching him sweep it up.
He holds the brush like a dancing partner,
short steps, fox trot: 4/4 time.
I knew from the first time, he did too.

Our eyes met when he came
to the bit above my lip. 6 years ago.
We've only slept the night together twice:
once when my wife's sister died,
once when the brother-in-law committed suicide.
She left our daughters behind that time.
My nerves made me come too quick
but I liked sleeping in his smooth arms
till dawn. He was gone

before they woke, giggling round breakfast.
He says nobody else can cut my curls.
I laughed loud for the first time since
God knows when. You're too vain man.
We kissed, I like his beard on my skin,
how can you be a barber with a beard
I said to him; it's my daughters that worry me.
Course I can never tell the boys down the pit.
When I'm down here I work fast so it hurts.

Unveiled nature

John Siddique

Veils to bring you to me. Love you
in with fineness. Promises of secrets.
A whiff of scent.

Veils to keep you from me. I shall not
pass this secret, shall not melt this gold.
This shroud protects a silent centre.

Veils to play with identity:
saint, ascetic, single, married.
Kali's hair denotes the time, showing
life and the end approaching.

Veils at pre-dawn to cover
the nakedness brought on
by such an early rise.

Afro Locks Glisten

Shirley May

I sit here longing

You hold court
The most noble
Subjects laid waste on the ground
Discarded play things

Pretending you were never beautiful
Yet walking past mirrors
You strike a pose

End of sentence, you lick
The corner of your mouth
Your tongue wilts pink
Co-conspirator
A cavern of testimony and slander

You remain always aloof.

Moon on open waters
Deep
Black
Pools
You lay waste your willing victims

Afro locks glisten
On pale opaque skin
You swear
She is your queen
Your new mooring.

Ms Ross

Kadija Sesay

He
Always
Implored me to look like Diana
Ross

I'd rather be bald.

Ombre

John Siddique

Her hair is a church.
Opening his guts to
worship at her.
To brush his hands
over her head.
To kiss her there
and there.

Kissing crowns,
lost in all softness.
Shampoo compulsion – dizzy,
remembering all that should
have been.
All he ever wanted in woman.

Hair in Neutral Tones

Jeanne Ellin

My hair has bled its colour to a neutral flag, signal not of surrender
but of a non-combatant in the sex wars saying 'No live ammunition here.'
But can we say the embraces of peace are less urgent, less alive?
The soft tolerance of twilight falls on folds and curves of winter land
secret sensuality waiting with no urgent fertility, just a friendly fire
waiting for encounters without the need for medals or casualties.

Two meanings

John Siddique

Loose hair marks the nubile state.

Bound,
she is married.

hair poem

Martin De Mello

skies
a last request close faded blue
god, what is left
he or she lights their final cigarette
my prayers magic balls
bouncing unheard
the harder i throw them
the harder and faster they come back

night
a cut moon needle perfect
doors swinging open divide into skies
i am naked
without instruction or parachute
the riddim inside
the riddim
mixing past lovers
while the dance floor explodes

then it happens

a star sign
close, faded blue in his eye
his mouth bloodied and not
the attraction
each ringlet an Indian prince
smelling of sandalwood, incense
a lost lifetime of reasons

not by fire, my trial: the liquor like darkness
and wet look of his gel

Private and Silently

SuAndi

I need to go home to look at my pubes
check them
inspect them
Naturally they are with me now
but this task is too intricate for
hotel rooms
a friend's futon
(read glorified and thin put-down settee)
or even the cosiest of spare rooms
I need to see my pubes
My routine
not too elaborate
leg over armchair
mirror placed carefully on thigh
reading lamp angled
in private and silently
Even if I could afford cosmetology
no skill could remove the grey I find there
an increasing shroud to my wilting womanhood
and so
I pluck and cry
pluck and cry

For Love's Sake

SuAndi

I wanted to write love poetry
So touch me here,
Where it hurts to inspire me.

Don't blow in my ear
That only chills me.
Touch me here,
Where it hurts to inspire me.

Please don't ruffle my hair,
And try to embrace not grapple with me.
And could you remove that stubble that you call a beard
Before you attempt to kiss me?

Take your elbow out my back;
And why are your knees so knobbly?
Did you know what you call muscles are really fat? –
And balding does nothing for me.

I can't write with feelings cold –
Come put your arms around me,
And touch me where it hurts
Honey, why are you choking me?

Great Hair

Deyika Nzeribe

Long black
Beautiful,
Fragrant...

A windswept charm
and a crown of light when you smile...
you have great hair.

I want it on
my clothes,
my bed,
my pillow,

I love it...
just
not
in
the bath...

A Photo

Nadeem Zafar

Middleton, Manchester, June 1978.
Standing outside my front door, the sun glowing on
    my face,
Casting its gaze on my mop of brown curly hair,
My father's red Suzuki motorcycle by my side.

I feel proud, the light cast over my locks flowing
    and shining
As though its own source of light, the strands like
Wire: strong and powerful, like nothing else on earth.

Seniors

Youth Passed

Mian Mohammad Bakhsh (tran Saeed Ahmed / Pete Kalu)

Aasey aasey gaee jawaanee fikar peyaa hun ehaa,
kaalyaan rang wataayaa goraa aayaa maot sunehyaa.

Youth passed, hoping against hope.
My black hair has turned grey
And I worry now that
It is a message of death.

Silver Top

Alanna Rice

Grandad used to ask
us to bring
hair dye
with us on
the plane.

Umecto
No. 1
Black.

The blackest
of blacks.

And now
at 86 (or 87)
he has
a
silver top.

Almost a sheen
of platinum curls.

Tightly covering
his fine
round head
like a
smattering of

icing sugar
on top
a rum
cake.

He had
a hair cut
yesterday.

Climbing the
steep
stairs atop
a chattel house
rum shop.

10 minutes
the man said
before
trimming the
already short
hair.

Silver curls
falling onto
wooden slats
like
dust on cleaning day.

You look smart Grandad.
But of course Lannie

As you climb
into the car.

The few
remaining hairs
on your knees
glistening in
the hot afternoon
sun.

To Hair with Love

Buzrak Mabrak

As if entranced, she would sit there,
Under the umbrella of the mango tree
On great grandma's ancient wooden stool,
That has sewed generations of hairs, hands,
Brushes and combs.
As the cool sea breeze ruffled the leaves,
With a flowing rhythmic motion,
The comb made pathways through her bushy locks,
Breaking the electromagnetic field that creates the
tangles in the kinks.
And if you could eclipse the sun and sounds,
You would hear the crackles and see the sparks fly,
Announcing their separation.

With her head tilting from one side to the other,
She would gently brush each strand,
Her brush, caressing, embracing, loving, caring.
And as she hummed a familiar sweet melody,
A bird nestled up above replied,
She smiled, eyes flickering black diamonds,
Her face at peace,
Her hair in unison with her hands.

Now, without mirror as guide,
With finger and comb, she parted her hair,
Creating perfect lots on either side.
Soon perfect lots became perfect plaits,
Her fingers with consummate skill and dexterity

Overlapping the strands of hair to their finest ends.

Then she would just sit there,
Smiling,
Pleased,
At ease.

So like clockwork,
Next week,
I will be back,
At ringside,
To watch with awe and pride,
As she does it all over again.

The Eternal Journey

Mian Mohammad Bakhsh (tran Saeed Ahmed / Pete Kalu)

Kaaley ik ik wichhar chaley gorey khat liyaaey.
Banho bhaar tiyaar safar da kooch sunehey aaey.

One by one my black hairs started leaving me.
Grey hairs have brought me a message -
to pack up and prepare for the Eternal Journey.

Sweet

Sheree Mack

Lime green rugby ball
like hot spitting coals when wrapper comes off
dull and ridged once in the mouth
still taste the plastic
with a soft mould around a hard core.

Bullets.
That's what Nana used to call them,
bullets.

She's have a stash of them in her handbag
reluctant to share, she was.
I'd be passing out with sickness
before she'd part with one.

'Make it last,' she'd say
popping another in her mouth.

A sweetness surrounded her
like the swirling candy floss at the Moor.

But like her wig
it was all artificial.

The Shave

SuAndi

I shaved my father once
when he had no interest to do so.
Held his head in my hand
and moved steel so sharp to murder
closer than close to his skin
wiped away the lather of white froth
to discover flesh so smooth
that age and he had no relationship
and kissed the handsome man
I found smiling proudly at me

A Sense of Passing

Sheree Mack

If I close my eyes
I can picture him,
in the bathroom mirror
clipping his close knit Afro
patting it down,
trying to see his handy work
from all angles;

Or him on an evening
ready for the Bookies
resting his trilby hat, just so,
as if it would fall off
but it doesn't.

If I listen carefully
I can hear him on the stairs
'Can it be that life was so simple then',
Roberta Flack style;

Or calling down to Eugene from the islands,
walking up Manchester Road.

If I sniff the air
I can catch a whiff of Old Spice
after Sunday chicken and rice.

Or the odour of iodine,
that disturbs our home.

The house rejects
with its frozen windows
dysfunctional heating.

Silk shirts we give away,
policies we keep.

Our time was short,
the sense lingers.

The Last Time

Anjum Malik

Sitting beside my father, I watched his face
He asked me to shave his beard
Lathering his stubble, I moved slowly
savouring the shape of his jaw, his lips
his perfect mouth, as he lay there
we talked, reminiscing of the days when
I stood by him as a little girl
shaving my pretend beard
and we laughed remembering how I cried
when I realised I would never have a beard
to shave, of my own
I combed his hair, parting at the side
With my palms I patted on his aftershave
He sat up laughing
I lit a cigarette and placed it between his lips
he laid back and exhaled, smoke swirled slowly
Time was moving fast
there was almost none left
the last time I saw him
he was holding my mother's hands
they were smiling at each other.

Hair Extension Trouble

Trudy Blake

I was worried
So I went to see mi doctor
A have dis lump pon mi face.
He send me to the hospital, for a X-ray.

Mi sit down pon de bench, and wait
for them to call me name
Then mi went innah this little room
The nurse sey to mi, yuh have plait in yuh hair.
Can yuh take this lot off?
No, a say, dem all tie up innah mi hair.

So she takes the X-ray.
And say wait outside.
In no time at all, she call me back.
You have pins in yuh hair
She accused mi.

So I feel all over mi head, a prodded mi scalp,
run mi finger all over mi hair, and ah think a
get dem all out, I couldn't believe it.
She called me back for the third time.
She sey a bit crossly, there's more more pins
in yuh hair. Suh a feel and ah search, and a
fine two more pins, ah don't know how I coulda
miss dem.

The nurse ask me, how many pins yuh fine?
Mi sey two, suh she take another picture, and me go outside and wait and mi hope all dem pins come out by now. All this struggle wih mi hair, with mi plait, and with these dam hair pins, mi only guh deh fe X-ray mi face, what a problem this plait hair giving me, it was a relief to know that it all come right in the end.

Illness

Kauser Parveen

It was illness that led her here
With the illness came many side effects
Amongst them hair loss
She did not become anxious
She held her head high
And embraced the change
'It will grow again,' she said
Never once did she feel defeated
She smiled
Plodded on with the adventure of life
The adventure of survival
The adventure of learning to live again

Myth, Mystery

My hair

Nyear Yaseen

Long and dark,
Like the Nile
Moving into the other life.

Mysterious
As clouds
Creating this season's mist.

Sexy and romantic,
Like the red corset worn
To pleasure a lover.

Secretive and masked,
Like a rose
Before it blooms.

Draped and fallen,
Like a whore
Who sleeps with wealthy men.

Coiffed and pinned,
Like the French,
Just before Napoleon's defeat.

Healthy and happy,
Like a poor child
Finally receiving his daily meal.

Our minds of golden heads

John Siddique

My daughter's hair is
a bird's nest
each morning
before school.

My hair is shaved short
pretending I have
a choice. The modern
version of the comb-over.

My brother/friend
is turning white,
he struggles with hair's
meaning.

On a white wall
a white plastic socket.
In a glass case
our minds of golden heads

bath nights

Sheree Mack

Because it reminded of Sunday bath nights
I loved the smell of warming wool
when condensation streamed down our bathroom
    mirror.

Because it reminded me of Sunday bath nights
my heart remembered
my mum washing my hair with vivid green shampoo.

Because it reminded me of Sunday bath nights
I loved the smell of warming wool
                    on radiators.

Twists

Deyika Nzeribe

Darkness twists
Around newborn
Stars
And into the
Black ones.

Darkness twists past
the quarks, atoms,
Molecules of carbon.

Dark twists through blood,
Muscle, skin.

And this
dark twist
of hair...

Both nothing
and a link to
Everything.

Oscillation

Dahu Mumagi

My hair was not a question
Until I changed space.
Then, every which way I wore it,
They'd laugh and ridicule.
Seemed peace could come only if
My hair was theirs.

With spiral motions stretching
From the beginning to the end of time
She sings to me, 'My hair is your blood!'
Her ans-astral Love
Swims in atoms and deep skies
Her hair is mine.

Dance with me, pride of magic curls,
On this special journey
Through the infinite black universe
Empty, void, well-spring of all.
Curling maximum to minimum
Galaxy to double helix
Dance with me, in this endless oscillation
Between ridicule and glory.

do not touch

Martin De Mello

early on I captured one thought:
pottery was like glass, dependent and fragile
stirring conflict, contempt and respect

I kept windows for the sole purpose
of obstructing my view
I counted fly footprints, the dust
left behind after rain
and wondered
at the world of the plateau
not beyond but too far to see

until the almanac fated I give birth to you

your skull, once the wax and the blood
were cleaned off, bone
not knitted and banana leaf thick, earthenware
baked in my kiln
with the subtlest fire of compassion
slopped on as the glaze

no honour or dishonour could break you
your head smooth as ghee
perfect and round and towards me indestructible

too old to sit at your feet, alter my ways
when you left I had one object
to give, separate
from the priest and the tradition of blessing

a grey strand, stubborn, without wisdom
yet sacred in this life and the next
as any easily broken and cast aside thread

Parasite

Aissatou Sylla

She took her time
To ensure she would be a Leo
I was long ready to come into the world.
Patient, I just kept on growing on her skull

When she came out at last
They all looked at her
And all caressed me
As they wrongly thought
My time as thin and silky was counted

Came Autumn, Winter and Spring
I was not changing,
They lost interest

But no one can take me for granted!

I wanted to cause a divorce
But despite my anorexic look
My host had her dad's cheekbones
I loathed hearing him rejoice 'Oh! C'est ma fille!'

They thought she was completely theirs
Fools!
No one can own me
Nothing can tame me.

Hair

Debjani Chatterjee

Look stranger, no further
behind the veil of this female.
My cascade of shimmering ringlets
encrusted with pearls, diademed with coral,
covers all the parts of me too awful to confront,
but is yet a mystery in itself.
Poor prince, I will let you climb up
my golden rope, never mind the pain.
But make no mistake –
this is not the means to some new beginning.
Have you the spirit to explore
its heart of darkness,
the forests that sprout like dragons' teeth
in lonely recesses of my woman's body,
the tropical bush that throbs with my blood beat
and provides the thorny wreath of death?
Yes, my crowning glory grows luxuriant,
even as I am strangling cell by cell.
These tresses contain a gorgon horror
that you cannot guess at in your Samsonest dream.
Look, I will let you comb this damask curtain;
stay, I will let you swim on its shining waves.
But remember that I am the lady
and it is my enchanted ladder you climb –
for I shall shake you off like vermin,
off with your head, smother you with my silken web,
when it is my sweet fancy and your adventure ends.

Entranced

Rashida Islam

I would see your ebony hair, lifted by the adoring
breeze,
And in those luxuriant waves I longed to twine a
garland
Of fragrant bel flowers. Like a bee, I was held
entranced.

Like a sunflower, many times I gazed upon your
lovely face,
Your dark tresses tumbling over enchanting eyes.
Like a shy deer in the shade, I observed you,
entranced.

I dreamed of the day when I would present you with
a spray
Of wild tuberose which you would tuck into your
plaited hair.
Not knowing how to capture your heart leaves me
entranced.

Several Springs came and went, and a special
moment arrived:
As if in a dream, I saw you at a concert, on a stage.
You were a star and your radiance kept me
entranced.

You floated down the aisle to accept the audience's
accolade,

And in a hushed and golden dream I walked
towards you.
Holding my offering of white flowers, I stood
entranced.

'Are these mine?' you smiled at me. But my flowers fell.
Where was the delicious twist of hair my flowers
would decorate?
Dismayed at your new boy-cut style, I stared
entranced.

Alas! How to reveal that I must now add this latest
episode
To my life's long list of fruitless efforts?
Your modern hair-style has left me speechless –
and entranced.

Moods of Hair

Usha Kishore

Prayer

Tresses of locks,
falling like the
blue-black waves
of the sea - a *tulsi*
leaf, stuck on the
tiny braid that holds
the ebb and flow -
a prayer to eternity
floats down in incense...

Marriage

Two hearts entwined
in braids, hanging
with jasmine garlands,
heralding the fragrance
of a tomorrow full of
love - gold jewels
dazzle in the dreams
of togetherness...

Seduction

In the light of the
oil-lamp, luscious
tendrils drip with
the intoxication
of henna and
sandalwood;

Jasmine blooms
smile seductively
at the approaching
night - lightning
flashes flirt with
the dark...

Mourning

Coils unravelled,
unravelled, flying
in the wind, beating
the air in anguish -
Fire burns in the
distance and *rudali*
song colours the
flowing grief ...

Tulsi - *Indian basil, used in Hindu worship.*
Rudali - *professional mourner from Rajasthan (North-Western India)*

Childhood & Children's Poems

New girl in school

Yvonne McCalla

my kinky hair elicits
a frisson
of excitement and fear
the curious at school
treating it like
an animal
at the zoo
patting it with
strange hesitation

maybe I should have kept it in a cage
and made them feed it...

Teasing The Hair

Rachel Van Den Bergen

Picky head.

Bushy head.

Sponge head.

Natty head.

Playground taunts.

Like ghosts they still haunt.

Can't you see I'm playing?

Pauline Omoboye

Can't you see I'm playing?
Don't part it like the railway track
Don't do my plaits too big
Don't ask me how I like it
Or if I'd prefer a wig
Don't press the comb hard on my scalp
Don't put in too much grease
Just leave it a jumbled mess
And leave me to my peace.

Hair To Stay

Pauline Omoboye

I wanted long hair
Flowing down my back
Flick it to the side
Part down the middle
hair

I wanted hair that's straight
Blow it in the wind
Straight through the brush
Not get tangled and stuck
hair

Hair that holds a clip
Slide through my fingers
Hair that's fair, not
Natty dread or pickie
hair

Not pretend with a cardigan
Hair that has a flair
Cut it in a bob
Do a 'Vosene ad'
hair

Yet now I love my

Took a while to understand
Curly tough and bouncy
My do-do plaits are my
hair

My afro big is smart
Coming from my 'roots'
A spring in my step is good
hair

Wash it shrink and stay
My hair is cool to wear
Not flyaway or blonde
hair

I'm told I have my mother's
Black and strong like me
What I'm proud to wear
hair

Rapunzel, Rapunzel

Elayne Ogbeta

Rapunzel, Rapunzel, my beauty so rare
Please will you let down your fine relaxed hair?

Oh no, dear Prince, I can't, I'm afraid,
For today I'm having my hair done in braids.

Rapunzel, Rapunzel, my beautiful maid
Can you please let down some of your braids?

Oh no, dear Prince, but would you believe!
On my dark head, I'm having a weave.

Rapunzel, Rapunzel, you I'll never leave.
Please will you let down your wonderful weave?

Oh no, dear Prince, oh please don't sqirm.
'Cause today I've decided to have me a perm.

Rapunzel, Rapunzel, my love I affirm
Can you please let down your ravishing perm?

Oh no, dear Prince, I could slap my wrists.
Did I not mention that I'm having a twist?

Rapunzel, Rapunzel, in my dreams I have kissed.
Please will you let down your elegant twists?

Oh no, dear Prince, I'm ever so slow.
I forgot to tell you I'm having a 'fro.

Rapunzel, Rapunzel, am I not your beau?
Could you please let down your soft afro?

Alas! Dear Prince but we cannot be wed.
The truth is my love, there's no hair on my head.

Bogeyman

Aissatou Sylla

If the monster comes in the night
Lay your head on my lap
My fingers edging into your whorls
Will vanish him in a twirl

If there is no monster in sight
Still lay your head in my lap
This caress on my palm
Is to me the perfect balm

Ghazal Couplets

Introduction

The ghazal is a popular type of short lyric poem in Urdu that can be set to music. It can be recited, chanted and sung, with or without musical accompaniment. Ghazals usually express love for the beloved – both sacred and profane. Often there are sentiments such as anguish or melancholy. Each individual couplet in a ghazal has the ability to be a complete and autonomous entity.

Great ghazal composers like Nasir Kazmi have enjoyed the adulation reserved in the West for pop stars, thanks not only to the *mushaira* performances – and a public *mushaira* can attract over a thousand listeners – but also to their work being sung by the greatest singers of the Indian sub-continent. Frequently, ghazals have been incorporated into Urdu and Hindi films: popular Indian and Pakistani cinema has a strong romantic streak and the ghazal is well suited to this medium.

Debjani Chatterjee

Asad-ullah Khan Ghalib - 1797-1869

Mangey hai phir kisi ko lub-e baam per haus
Zulf-e siyah rukh pe pareshaan kiye hoey

Once more desire wants someone at the roof edge,
her black tresses dishevelled across her face.

Asad-ullah Khan Ghalib - 1797-1869

Neend os ki hai dimagh os ka hai raatein os ki hein
Teri zulfein jis ke baazo per pareshaan ho gaeen

The intellect, the night and sleep, are his
on whose arm your tresses lie dishevelled.

Basir Sultan Kazmi - b. 1955-

Ab to ganwa rehey ho shab-o roze khaab mein
Phir dhondtey phiro ge jawanee khizaab mein

Now you waste your days and nights in sleep;
someday you'll look for youth in hair dye.

Momin Khan Momin - 1801-1852

Kis ki zulfon ka dhiyan tha ke mein shub
Mahw-e dood-e chiragh-e khana raha

Whose locks was I contemplating last night that
I remained absorbed in the house-lamp's smoke?

Asad-ullah Khan Ghalib - 1797-1869

Wo aur aaraayish-e kham-e kaakul
Mein aur undesha ha-ey door daraz

She adorns the ringlets of her hair
and my thoughts transport me far away.

Mir Taqi Mir - 1722-1810

Hum hoey tum hoey ke Mir Hoey
Os ki zulfon ke sub aseer hoey

Whether it's me or you or Mir,
All are captivated by her curls.

Ghulam Hamdani Mushafi - 1750-1824

Yaan la'l-e-fusun saaz ne baaton mein lagaya
De paich odher zulf ura le gaee dil ko

The spellbinding ruby held me in talk,
as her curls ensnared and pillaged my heart.

Nasir Kazmi - 1925-1972

Hamarey ghar ki deewaron pe Nasir
Odaasi baal kholey so rahi hai

On the walls of our dwelling, Nasir,
Melancholy sleeps with unkempt hair.

Nasir Kazmi - 1925-1972

Naey kaprey badal ker jaaon kahan aur baal
banaoon kis ke liyey
Wo shakhs to shehr hi chor gaya mein baher
jaaon kis ke liyey

Donning new clothes, where should I go and for
whom should I groom my hair?
That person has left the city altogether, so for
whom should I go out?

Nasir Kazmi - 1925-1972

Terey baalon ki khushboo sey
saara aangan mehek raha tha

With the fragrance of your hair
The whole courtyard was perfumed.

Ahmed Mushtaq - b. 1933-

Wo chalti to hawa os key kholey baalon mein
chalti thi
Kabhi baadal omadtey they kabhi sooraj nikalta tha

When she walked, the wind blew in her unbound hair.
Sometimes clouds would appear and sometimes
the sun.

Ahmed Mushtaq - b. 1933-

Yaar sub jumm hoey raat ki taareeki mein
Koi ro ker to koi baal bana ker aaya

Friends all gathered in the darkness of the night;
some had wept while some had combed their hair
and come.

Ahmed Mushtaq - b. 1933-

Zulf dekhi wo dhuaan daar wo chehra dekha
Such bata dekhne waaley osey kesa dekha

Did you see those smoke-dark tresses? That face?
Observer, be frank - how did you find her?

Basir Sultan Kazmi - b. 1955-

Leiti theen ghataaen jin se rung
Muhtaaj-e khizaab ho gaey hein

The locks that lent their colour to dark clouds
Are now themselves dependent on a dye.

Short Stories

Ma's Wig

Tanya Chan Sam

I always slept in Ma's bed, cuddled up to her soft cool, fleshy arms. One night after her bedtime story she said, 'You're a big girl, aren't you? I have a secret just for you.'

I looked intently into her eyes behind the tortoiseshell rimmed spectacles, perched on the end of her nose. Ma guided my hand onto my heart, my finger on my lips, as I nodded my head to an oath that I would never tell anyone, ever, what I was about to see.

Ma lifted her hair. Right off her head. I kept my forefinger pressed tightly against my gaping mouth.

'It's a wig.' she mouthed.

'Oh,' I said through barred lips.

I could see Ma's own hair. Thick, coarse, grey hairs twisted into braids, which she unravelled quickly, her fingers widespread as she fluffed out the crinkly strands. My hand reached forward to touch the tendrils dangling against her wrinkled neck.

'Uh huh, don't,' she slapped at my fingers. I sucked on my nails and watched her fork through her hair with a wide tooth comb. It made rough scraping noises as she dragged the teeth across her scalp.

That night started my apprenticeship of wig duty. My responsibility was to keep a vigil, to warn her of any hairs showing. *'The vagrants,'* she called them. To alert her, I would swivel my eyes from left to right and finger the side of my head to let her know which side her natural hairs were emerging. Ma would try to tuck them back, gripping the wig with her middle finger and shoving the *vagrants* back inside with her forefinger.

One Saturday morning, we were in Claremont laden with shopping bags. We joined the long queues at the bus terminus, already snaking past the pissy subway steps. Trains thundered through, conductors shouting out destinations, '...Rondebosch, Mowbray, Salt River, Kaapstad!' followed by screeching whistles. Hawkers rustled fuzzy peaches into brown paper bags and juggled change in their big pockets.

We moved slowly, heaving the shopping bags a few steps at a time. Suddenly we were pushed into a huddle; bums and large rumps colliding with my head. When I looked up, four or five skollies stood around us. The tallest one spoke.

'OK mummies, stan' now still. You've all lekker done your shopping. Give now also for us. Don't shout, and you'se won't get hurt.'

I felt Ma's hand on my shoulder pulling me close. Her wide hips covered in green crimplene obscured my view so I craned my neck around her thigh to get a better look. Sunlight caught the gold slit between the skollie's full lips as he smiled broadly at Ma. She held her purse out towards him, her thumb and forefinger gripping the tiny brass clasp. He stared into Ma's eyes, blinking behind her tortoise shell rimmed spectacles, not at the purse, trembling in her outstretched palm. He placed his large brown hand over hers, rubbing from side to side. His wide mouth opened as his tongue curled into a pink tip sucking at the gold slit.

'I know where auntie is keeping auntie's money.'

His eyes lifted to the crown of her head and he bobbed delicately. In one smooth movement, he tucked his hands into his armpits, and spun on his heels, turning his tall back on us. I watched his long fingers emerge onto his back and drum lightly against the cloth of his printed shirt. The sinews on his neck stretched first left, then right, as he looked up and down the queue, while Ma's hand reached under her wig and gingerly tweezed out two banknotes with her thumb and forefinger.

She yanked at my shoulder and hissed, 'Look for *vagrants*!'

I worked furiously and furtively, my eyes darting around her hairline, my fingers surreptitiously pointing to the *vagrants*. Only once I'd nodded my head to signal all was in place, did she tap the skollie on the shoulder and hand over the notes.

Pinto the Barber

Vijay Medtia

Placing the clean white sheet very carefully over the body and around the collar, and then tying the strings behind the neck, Das Pinto's practiced hands mixed the white shaving foam with a small brush. He started to apply the foam with the brush onto the young man's face, watching him carefully; he then took his sharp razor in his right hand and tilted the man's head to one side slightly, before bringing the razor in touch with the man's skin. A smooth stroke, and then he repeated it again before pausing for a moment, as the fresh smell of foam surrounded them. He then glanced in the mirror before looking down at the young man.

'I would say you were the two year sort, not more than four.'

'I beg your pardon?' said the young man, whose name was Raja, a little taken by the odd statement.

Pinto brought the razor downwards from the chin following the line of the neck, wiped it on a clean white towel and dipped the razor in some warm water before starting again. 'I think you've served two years, yes two years- am I correct?'

Raja didn't like the line of questioning but he was impressed by the barber's assumption, and his curiosity arose, so he agreed to talk. 'Yes, you're correct. But how did you know?'

'I've been doing this for over twenty years! I can tell what sort of person sits in my chair from the moment he enters my shop, and I'm very rarely wrong.' He continued to use the steel razor with precision, not a single cut.

'If I may- I would guess that you committed some small fraud or robbery at best, nothing too serious.'

Now Raja was totally impressed, he was in the hands of a master. He was right, he had been involved in a small fraud for which he was given two years.

'Yes, you are correct,' he said.

Pinto finished shaving him, and then quickly trimmed his hair; when Raja stood up from the chair Pinto looked at him with a smile and said, 'Now you look like a real Raja, truly a prince!'

Raja looked in the mirror with satisfaction, he looked completely different; he stroked his smooth face before asking, 'Yes, but how do you know?'

Pinto placed the tools of his trade onto the counter and said slowly, 'Take a look.' He pointed across the road to the Central Government Prison. 'I'm the first shop when you leave. It's location, always location. I have the best place, and the second thing is you still have considerable hope in your eyes. If you had served a longer time you would look different, your eyes would be flat, lifeless.'

Pinto stretched out his hand, 'That will be fifteen rupees.'

Raja gave him twenty and started to leave with a smile.

'I hope I don't see you again,' said Pinto.

'You won't,' said Raja.

Childhood Hair

Rowena Fan

My hair is fragile, thin and white. It is as old as me.

It's nearly past my chin and covers up the pink balding patches underneath. I wash it ever so gently, with a mossy green shampoo; my daughter says it helps keep the scalp healthy. My granddaughter has developed a new habit of tugging on the thin strands. I can't smack her; my daughter objects, so the mischievous rascal continues to pull out odd strands, every Sunday afternoon. When she's gone, I see my hair, lonely trails on the sofa.

There was a time when my hair was the envy of my village. It was never cut, it grew and grew. Other girls had long hair too, but mine was the strongest and the shiniest. My second aunt, from Quaidong village used to say that all that vitamins I ate must've been sucked up by my hair. My mother said it would guarantee me a good suitor, as my future husband would want to show me off. She would tell me about the pre-marital night, how she would have to brush my hair, an ancient ritual signalling my womanhood.

Once, one of the bigger girls dared me to tie the end of my hair to a bucket, and pull water up from a deep well. So I double knotted my hair onto the handle of the wooden bucket and began to lower it slowly. Thirty young children watched me as I cockily lowered my hair, and I tried, whilst biting my lip, to scoop up as much water as possible.

The true weight of water shocked me and I could feel my hair tugging and tugging, the pain was becoming so intense. 'Help me!' I yelled, whilst the other children watched dumbstruck.

My options. Have my hair cut off. Stand there and let the hair tear out of my scalp, just to show how tough I was. Or I could jump into the well to preserve my hair, but severely hurt myself.

My choice?

Well, I have a limp, even to this day.

But I did have beautiful hair.

I remember

Pev V'vshh

I'm scratching my suede head. Ah, yes, now I remember...

The very first time was in Panama. Out came shiny new clippers and they were soon chewing through my long hair. If I'm honest, it was painful – but it was receding and besides, what can you expect for ten dollars? But, y'know, it felt good too. The vibrations on my skull buzzuzzummed deep down into my brain – a strange central purring sensation.

As the years have gone by the initial mirror-shock of subtraction has receded too. Now I prefer the reflection of my naked, unadorned head: me, myself and I and I, pure and simple.

Someone once said that hairs are your aerials, but I think hairs are switches connected to memory cells inside your brain. When I wiggle a certain bristle it triggers a certain memory.

I scratch my head, then the smell of boiling beans...and the sound of sizzling chicken...and the foam of the sea...and the taste of her neck...and...and...and...

Why else would people scratch their heads when they want to think?

Copper Inna Red Head

Shirley May

One thing grandfather couldn't stand was a thief in the house. There was a time when too many things were going missing and my grandparents decided to do something about it. Grandmother dealt with all the household payment and shopping. She was constantly dipping in and out of her purse to pay for provisions. Sparrow the carpenter man had called in to deliver a new stool that my grandmother had ordered from him in the week. Instead of opening the purse and dropping the penny change inside it, my grandmother put her purse into her apron pocket and put the penny on a corner of the dresser. Over the course of the day, it duly went missing.

There was twelve of them but one dead left eleven. I suppose with eleven in the house anybody could have taken it. They were all lined up and interrogated. I don't know if they all came up with their alibis. I have a photograph of my grandfather who looks quite stern. Everyone lined up in front of him and emptied their pockets. They had names like Merryman, Huntley, and Papason, strange names like that.

Edith who is called Sister had taken the penny and hidden it between one of her plaits. It's her turn to be inspected but nothing is found and she's sent on her way.

She forgot the penny, thought she had got clean away and went about the day, until my grandmother called her to comb out her hair. As her mother undoes each plait, working from the back towards the front, Edith suddenly remembers, panics and tries to move away. If you've ever had your hair combed out you'll know that once between those legs you can't move and despite her protest she is held fast.

After that, she was the thief in the house - Copper Inna Red Head. If anything went missing they would look to Sister first, letting her know their suspicions by the look in their eyes.

Monday At The Barber's

G Ovie Jobome

Monday has a most unfortunate shape of head. Kind of angled at the top towards the back and slightly tapered at the front around the middle. The overall effect is like a wonky triangle. His visits to his barber are quite fraught. He tries to achieve the most rounded look possible to his head, that usually means leaning towards an Afro hairstyle to have a head shape that looks vaguely normal. He roped me along on a visit one time. Never again.

We reach Lambo's and step in. *I-wanna-sex-you-up* blares from the speakers hung close to the ceiling. Posters cover all walls, floor to ceiling. Picture posters. Beaches. Palm trees. American rappers. And Calendars; I think you know what's on them. The hot seat becomes vacant. Monday settles in. All begins well. A confident and peaceful snip snip snipping. Suddenly Monday jerks to life, peering closely into the mirrors that surround him then motioning to Lambo the Barber.

'I tink you have taken enough hair off dat side now.'

'I know what am doing. I have been doing this since before your time.' Lambo.

'Okay, okay, but try not to go too low on dat side.'

'I hear you…I hear.'

Smidgens of foamy spit gather at both corners of Lambo the Barber's mouth as he relates the one about Solo and his wife Becky. Apparently, Solo's wife was accused by her own brother of being a witch. Lambo swears he was there at the time, spittle spraying. But Solo was a Born-Again and did not believe in witchcraft, and all entreaties to abandon the crazy plan to marry Becky fell on deaf ears. His mother even threatened to disown him if the marriage went ahead. Solo moved from home, and swore never to see his mother again and that nothing will stand between him and his lovely Becky.

'Enough from that side.' Monday interrupts.

'I hear you...'

Lambo resumes. And so the love affair went on. But it wasn't your usual love affair. Being a Born-Again, there was no question of sex before marriage for Solo. Apparently, they did everything but. Very heavy kissing. Very heavy rubbing. Very heavy... Lambo doesn't explain who it was that actually did the research on the sex behaviour of the two lovers. One does not ask such questions. Anyway, Becky got pregnant. Heavy petting gone wrong, some concluded. It's the devil's child, others were convinced.

'Hey man! Never mind about that, I said enough from dat side. Now look! Shit. Dis isn't working is it?'

'But it has to be balanced with the other side.' The barber, exasperated.

'Yes balanced. Dat doesn't mean you should shave my head bald.'

'You exaggerate a bit, don't you? You can hardly call this bald...'

Now Solo might have been a Born-Again. But he

was also pragmatic. He did not have sex with this woman. Not really. Who is to question God's wisdom in these things...? So the marriage was arranged swiftly, before Becky's bump set tongues wagging. Lambo assures his audience that the Pastor raised his eyebrows at the undue haste, but acquiesced in the end. Everyone, he says, was sure the union was doomed, what with Becky being a certified witch, and Solo a Born-Again estranged from his own mother. But surprisingly the wedding went without hitch, the all-singing all-dancing congregation masked the absence of both the bride's and the groom's parents. Becky's machete-wielding brother turned up after the service was concluded. Turns out the banns deliberately misprinted the time of the wedding, to thwart the intentions of unbelievers and the devil's agents...

'Oh shit! Now you've gone and done it on de oder side as well! Shit man.'

'But you just agreed it has to be balanced.'

'But I didn't want all dat part coming off. Now look... .'

'Excuse me, but you came to me for a haircut, didn't you?'

'Yes. Haircut. Not to be plucked clean like a fowl.'

'Well if you say I can't cut any hair then what's the point?'

'You are meant to just take a little off at de back and front and den leave de rest pretty much as is – like I explained to you at de beginning.'

'Ohhhh! You mean like an Afro?'

'I didn't say Afro.'

Anyway. Lambo presses on with his story. Becky grew very big. She exploded. Her eyes sank deep into fleshy folds of eyebrow overhang. Her legs became like an elephant's. Solo's Christian sisters tended to her round the clock. And still she swelled.

'Mind my head! Now you've cut far too much from dat side. What's wrong wit you?!' Monday screams at the mirror, leaning out of Lambo's reach.

'I'm sorry but Afro is out of fashion, even I... .'

'What a fool. First of all you fuck up my hair. Den you fuck up my head. And you're trying to find weak excuses... .'

'Listen young man if you must know, there's only so much a barber can do with a head like yours. Anything more and you're asking me to play God.'

'You moron. You shall pay for dis...with dis! And dis!' That's Lambo the Barber's clippers and shaving set smashed to pieces and stamped upon.

'Vagabond! I'll call the police! Idiot... son of a witch...devil seed...' Lambo raves, tearing at his greying hair and jabbing an impotent finger in Monday's direction, spittle flying everywhere.

'Come on, let's go...before I do dis fool permanent damage.' Monday, to me.

'Son of a devil whore...the devil screwed your mother...!' That's his last words to that barber.

Last I heard, he was running out of barbers.

Pipe Cleaner Perms

Seni Seneviratne

Maybe my soft curls were shock waves after a traumatic Caesarean birth, but I was the only one in our family born with curly hair. They stuck out from under my fluffy bonnets when I was a baby. They pointed wildly in every direction during my early toddler days. By the time I was three, my hair was long enough to be pulled tight from a straight side parting into a bow as big as my head. Clips and an assortment of slides sorted the stray hairs. Eventually my curls gave up. There was only a hint of them in my straight hair.

I was five when they re-appeared again. It was the mid fifties and my mother had discovered home perm kits, Toni, Rayve, Bobbi, Twink. She tried them all, not only on herself but on me and my older sister. Over the next seven years any special occasion was preceded by the pungent ritual of home-perming. First communions, Whitsuntide, Christmas family gatherings are all tinged with the odour of perm solution.

The smell, ammonium thioglycolate, was more putrid than a stink bomb. I sat gagging in the fumes beneath my mother's swift fingers. She sponged small strands of hair with the alkaline solution, wrapped them in tissue end-papers and rolled them up in off-white pipe cleaners, flat against my head. When my head was covered in rows of these makeshift curlers right up to my parting, she dabbed what was left of the liquid all over my head. A cold, stinging shock to my scalp. Then out came the Morphy Richards hair dryer. A heavy instrument of moulded ivory plastic that scared me with its noise and the red filaments inside its nozzle. My head fried under its relentless heat.

At every stage of the process my five year old body fidgeted. I shifted around on the seat, scratched the tickles in my bottom, swung my legs over the edge of the dining room chair, but my head was held still by the firm grip of my mother's hands. Eyes closed tight against the sting, nose wrinkled against the stench, I savoured the anticipation of the froth of frizzy curls that would billow from my side parting when it was all done.

All your strength is going to your hair

Jeanne Ellin

'You are my white mouse,' my mother said, brushing my thin flat hair. Her's was thick, dark-strong with a rising wave that needed nothing to lift it. My sister had her dark skin and that rich hair.

Our downstairs neighbours had two teenage girls who were kind to me. The elder had skin like a peeled almond and hair that lay flat and brown like mine, she was sweet but not pretty, I thought. Her sister had hair like a raincloud, dark and full of curves when it was unplaited. They were talking about getting married, how their father was searching for good husbands for them. The younger sister said that she knew it would be hard for her father to get a good match for her. I asked why since she was so pretty? Because she was too dark, she said.

Later, I grew my hair in plaits like the sisters and the plaits were thick as my bony wrists and it was a comfort to suck the ends and when the plaits were loose I had waves in my hair too. When my plaits reached the small of my back, before my eighth birthday, my father died and we went to England, the *home* we had never seen.

I had been told not to cry as it would upset my mother, so I never did. But in England my Aunt got my hair cut. 'All your strength is going to your hair, you are too skinny,' she said, and dressed me in an English camel-coat. I thought some spitting camel had been skinned for it; I looked in the mirror and cried.

The Passionate Lover

Martin de Mello

Kyle was shorter than everyone expected, and not quite as handsome. He was, however, very dark, being one quarter Algerian, half Irish and a quarter from somewhere near Sierra Leone. His lips were unusually fine and had a pout that made her instantly want to kiss them. His eyebrows were pencil lines. Long before they'd gotten married he would lie with his head in her lap while she gently plucked them, shaping two sculpted brows. Afterwards she'd remove her glasses and bend so close she could see each individual pore on his forehead and the tiny, invisible hairs on his nose. She adored those hairs, they reminded her of three month old babies that she wanted to hug until she had squeezed the little creatures into her heart. She could hardly wait to finish so that she could tease her lips against his, and give him the added pleasure of having his face buried in her voluptuous breasts.

Those days were now gone. Kyle plucked his own eyebrows every Sunday and was simply letting her know that he was off to work. He had a job at the gas works, as far as she understood maintaining the pipes, though he got annoyed when she described it as that. He preferred to describe himself as *more of an engineer*.

'Wait a minute.'

He waited, two tiny brackets on the ends of his mouth telling her that he knew what was coming.

'Where did I put my tweezers?'

He suggested the bathroom. She had recently developed the habit of using them to pink her toes, a reminder of the time when she bit her toenails.

She returned, tweezers between thumb and forefinger, waving them excitedly.

'I've got them, now lean back.'

Delicately she teased into view one of his nostril hairs and plucked it at the root. He winked, not so much in pain, and brought his perfect lips together, kissing her on the cheekbone.

The door shut, Sanrevelle put the freshly plucked hair in the matchbox she kept for the purpose. She had six matchboxes now, going back fifteen years.

Annapurna

Tara Chatterjee

In her eighties, Dida, my grandmother, had long black hair with a few silvery streaks. She had plenty of family tales to enthral us children. Dida became a child-bride at nine. Dadu, my grandfather, was eighteen and at Calcutta University. He later held various lecturing posts. My grandparents were pious and loved to go on pilgrimage.

Their fourth child – born on an auspicious day – was named 'Annapurna' ('The Giver of Food'), in honour of the Mother Goddess. This daughter was conceived in the holy city of Benaras. The baby's head was a mass of black and unusually long curls – just like that of the Goddess Annapurna. People came to marvel. The hair was so tightly curled that Dida had great difficulty combing it. 'Why didn't God give you straight hair like that of your brothers and sisters!' she would say. Many Hindus shave a child's head at eighteen months. Dida was waiting for this and determined to keep Annapurna's unruly hair trimmed short afterwards.

Annapurna was eleven months old when the family returned to Benaras as pilgrims. They bathed in the Ganges at dawn before visiting the temple. One by one, Dadu lifted the three older children so that each could experience the thrill of ringing the bronze bell that hung at the entrance. The family gazed at the small sculpture of the beautiful goddess. Although smothered in garlands of fragrant marigolds and roses, the serene face of the goddess with its halo of frizzy hair was clearly visible. Many morning worshippers stared at both the goddess and at the baby Annapurna. Dadu chanted a hymn of praise, while Dida said a quick private prayer. A kindly priest gave them leaf-bowls with pieces of fruit and sweets. Dadu then sat down to meditate for an hour or so, while Dida found a corner of the prayer hall where she spread a towel on the marble floor for their now sleeping baby. She also kept a watchful eye on the boisterous older children as they played among the pillars.

Suddenly Annapurna screamed. Dadu's meditation broke and he came running. Dida, the other children and everyone in the temple rushed to her. Dida lifted up her baby to cuddle her.But her stroking fingers on her daughter's hair froze and she shrieked in alarm. The infant's knotted hair had gone! In its place was silky straight black hair! Many present had noticed the baby's unusually curly tresses, and they were all now amazed. People offered explanations. One insisted that the child was possessed by the spirit of the goddess and should be worshipped. Others disagreed, saying that she had been possessed, but her straight hair was now evidence that the goddess had left her. Some said that Dida must have prayed for her daughter's hair to be straightened – and everyone knew that prayers are powerful. But my grandparents remained mystified when they left Benaras.

From then onwards Annapurna became quiet and sickly. Fourteen years after the strange incident at the temple, she caught typhoid and left this world

– it was the winter of 1934. While she lived she had luxuriant hair – silky, long and black. But, like Dida's, it was also straight – quite unlike that of the Goddess Annapurna.

Liam Gets His Hair Cut

Peter Kalu

Why did barbers become barbers? Who would choose to stand all day for a living wielding a pair of scaled down sheep shears, your feet tramping across a floor of split hairs and dandruff, condemned to listen to the twin babble of local youth an old-timers, your lungs constantly breathing in jasmine scented oil spray and the breath off those that chose to eat Pattyman's crusty meat patties at 3am the night before, your tea encrusted with little black hairs, your clothes encrusted with little black hairs, the shine of your shoes dimmed by little black hairs, all fallen from the pates of your shallow pocketed customers, an those pates are your only view for the full eight hours of your standing, scissoring, fluffing, coughing day. Why?

Well when you observed that all barbers in the area were seriously bald, you could figure this one out without phoning the Premium Number Helpline, right? They became barbers because that way they got a peep hole into the world of people with hair. That was my theory anyway.

When it came to my turn at Mustafa's, I was in the padded swivel chair like a Chinese rocket. He knocked the chair lower cos it was a kid he was doing before me, swished the huge plastic bib thing round my neck so it floated over my front, then nudged my head for a ritual inspection of my hair, as his small talk kicked in:

'How's things, my boy?'

'Everything's buff, Pops.'

'Wind been whislin thru your hair, nights?'

'Been plastered to me forehead mostly, wiv the rain.'

'Frost been freezin it?'

'Right, even indoors it wasn't meltin.'

'What do you do? Wrap a towel around?'

'Got the blow dryer out.'

Mustafa tutted. 'I don't believe in those machines. Soulless. An Afro like yours deserves respect. Judicious treatement. Blow dry is not something I recommend fuh none of mah customers, no. Blow dry? There should be a.. a ..hact of Parlament.'

'Law against?'

'Right. It's a crime. along wid murder, mayhem an no tax disc. Invented by a bald man, hair dryers, a bald man seekin revenge, yuh hunderstan?'

'That's a good one, Mustafa, comin from you.'

Mustafa stroked his polished, patchily oiled dome and cracked a grin. His three waiting customers an me grinned with him.

'Li-yam's yuh name?'

'Bang on.'

'But you don' look after yuh hair good, Li-yam. Youth wasted on the young. Hair wasted on dem too.'

His customers on the bench, who could put in two hundred years between them, had another good guffaw. Mustafa kept it up as he ran though his scissorin-sprayin-Afro combin-more sprayin - sweepin - nudgin - primpin - levellin-more scissorin -more sprayin - an finally lookin satisfied- routine.

He held a small mirror up so I could check the back of me head. I nodded and he lowered the mirror. I climbed out the chair an paid him. 'By the way,' I asked, casual like, 'is your Anthony around?'

Mustafa snorted, but thought about it. While he did, an old timer with a thick carpet of straight out of a 70's knitting catalogue grey hair, snuck into the business seat.

'Not sure, but you could try Tracy's,' Mustafa said. 'He's either wid Tracy or...' His voice trailed off. 'Don't you go getting him into no more trouble, y'hear, Li-yam?'

'Course I won't,' I said. 'And thanks for this, you know man, it's cool.'

He waved me away. 'Look after it now,' he called.

Mustafa wasn't a major fan of me, but he did have a soft spot for my hair.

Mi Natty Dred Don Gimme Art'ritis

Simon Murray

Buk, buk, yes bwoy! Mi luk baaad nuh.
My new hairstyle is most becoming, is it not?

Eaaasy-like. Nu-need fuh nuh foolishness an ting.
Yes, there is now no need to visit the barber and I can cut down on hair-care products thereby helping the environment. Plus, all in all it saves myself both time and expense.

Me's a baad bwoy yuh nuh. Why yu nuh cum check mi gal?
You know, I might even be able to attract some favourable female attention.

Man step tuh mi, tell mi: whappen yuh hair? Him prefer dat fool Wacko Jacko and hi batty 'fro.
Well, I'm not entirely certain my boss appreciated the "new look".

i and i is mi dred mi tell he. Mi dred is i.
He intimated that I should remove my Rasta hat.

Man can tell mi shit. Mon, i tells he: go fuck. Yah, go fuck ya stink eye job, go fuck. i is a breddren yuh hear? i is a dredlock yuh si? Nuh patty-hair sell-out wigga lickle bwoy – i is a Bob Marley dredlock rasta revalueshan yuh hear!
His request displeased me somewhat but with

reluctance I did of course consent.

Si well now, now mi got di pain inni han.

Well, it would indeed seem that my boss was correct – the role of data programmer really is not compatible with a street urban hair-style. Yes, the tapping of keyboards, moving of a computer mouse and the twisting of locks of hair has resulted in my contracting repetitive strain injury.

I gun leave hi bombaclart job si. i gun Afrika y'anuh. fine man root. wuk di lan. One love. One life. Jah rastafari.

The upshot is: I've been advised by the physiotherapist to take sick-leave and let my RSI clear up. I'm thinking of booking a relaxing week in Gran Canaria.

De dred roll on rude bwoy, di dred roll on.

In retrospect: I should have stuck with my flat-top.

Problem Pages With Khadija Rehman

Help! All my daughters have started to look prettier than me with their flowing black hair which they constantly flick. Despite my better nature, I can't stop feeling jealous. Do I need therapy or is this a normal feeling for mothers?

Your feelings are very normal for a woman who is going into a different phase of life where all of sudden everyone seems younger and prettier. No matter how hard you try to come to terms with the knowledge that you are getting bit older, the loss of youth still catches you out and looking at your girls bring this home. The jealousy feeling is towards the bygone years and not your daughters.

You must try to remember that your girls possessing this beauty is due to the good genes that you have passed down to them. Also if you are honest with yourself you probably have had your share of beauty and flowing locks and are still beautiful. It could be that you have stopped noticing.

You have now developed more inner beauty which is replenishing some of the faded exterior beauty. I'm sure from your experience and wisdom you have learnt that it's the inside of the person that matters more than the outside.

One other explanation could be that you might be suffering from low self-esteem or have a low image of yourself which needs improving. So seek out some groups which can help you to build on your positive qualities. Try joining some social clubs with similar age people. Being surrounded by people of the same age will help you accept your looks as a normal part of life. Life is too short to worry about what you have lost or are losing. Instead you should focus on what you have gained or are gaining with the passing of time.

I had a No 1 haircut at my barbers with the Pakistan flag cut into it, but my school sent me home. Is this discrimination? How much can I sue them for and will it pay for tickets to see Manchester United?

Young people like doing things which make them stand out but sometimes this can cause problems in education or working environments. Schools have rules and regulations in place to ensure the safety of their pupils, and students have a responsibility to respect and maintain these while they are at school, including being dressed according to the rules too. This might not please young people but it is good for them in the long run as they will be learning how to obey and respect rules in other areas of their life.

Regarding discrimination, this would be a discrimination issue if your peers have similar hairstyles but you were the only one sent home. This would be evidence that you were being treated unfairly compared to others. As far as the money is concerned, I think there are lots of other ways you can make money by using your creative mind that will involve much less hassle.

Good luck to you and your football team.

How do I know if my barber uses clean shears and scissors? I'm scared of getting an infection.

It is not easy to identify clean or unclean equipment because germs are microscopic and so hard to see. Businesses are regulated to make sure they maintain a certain level of hygiene for the safety of their customers. Your barbers shop should reflect this in their standard of cleanliness, so have a careful look around next time you go. Also you are allowed to ask questions about any concerns you have and can even inspect their Health and Safety Certificate to make sure it is up to date. If you still feel your barber shop is not keeping to the standard required, then you are within your rights to report it to prevent other people from harm.

Hygiene is an important aspect of your life that needs to be observed, but at the same time you need to make sure it doesn't become an obsession. Try to reflect and see how you feel about cleanliness and hygiene in general: are you overly concerned about this issue? If so, you might need further help so see your GP or talk to someone at your local Health Centre.

My father is bald on top and does a Bobby Charlton style comb-over to hide it. Will I go bald like that too? I'd rather die.

I am sorry to hear you are stressed about the unknown future of your hair and I'm afraid this is something that no one will be able to tell you with absolute certainty.

Scientists, as you know, say children inherit genes from their parents. These genes produce some good results and some not so good. Early hair loss could be one of them, but take hope that the chances are perhaps also equal that you might not take after your father in this respect – you might not go bald. Hair loss can be quite traumatic and people deal with it in different ways. Some come to accept it. Others try to find ways of making the most of the hair that is left.

As you can see how devastated you feel at just the thought of losing hair, so you can imagine what it must be like for your father to actually lose it. So try to show some sympathy towards your dad who in his own way is trying to come to terms with his hair loss and is using alternative methods to disguise this.

No matter how one feels, no one actually dies following hair loss, so try not to stress yourself too much because stress can sometimes cause hair loss. Try to get on with your life as best as possible and if it does happen to you then you will hopefully be more secure in yourself and able to deal with it.

Styling Tips
With Shirley May & Pete Kalu

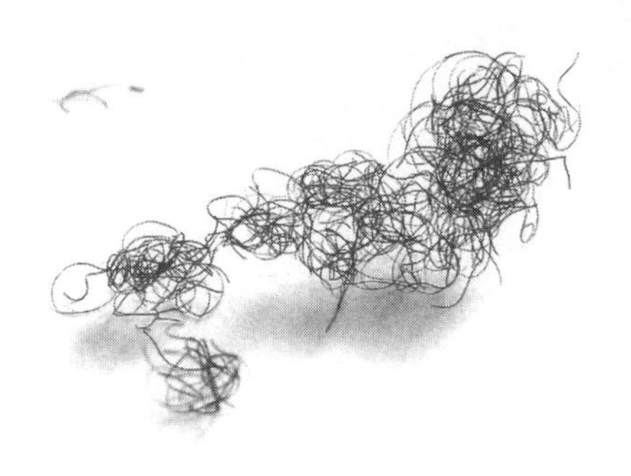

How To Do Basic Rope Twists

Use a large toothed comb to detangle hair.
Part hair into sections.
You need in the region of 100 sections for a full head of rope twists.
Divide hair within one section into two bunches. (This is a fundamental difference between braids, which you divide into three).
Holding hair firmly, twist hair bunches left over right (or right over left).
Continuing until you reach the end of the strands of hair.
Repeat for the other 99 sections.
You have now done a full head of rope twists.

* * * * *

How To Plait Hair

Use a large toothed comb to detangle hair.
Part hair into sections.
Divide the hair within one section into three bunches.
Hold the middle and end bunch in your right hand.
Hold the other bunch in your left hand.
Then cross the end bunch over the middle bunch.
Cross the left hand bunch over what is now the new middle bunch.
Repeat these steps all the way down the shaft of hair
Until you reach the hair ends.
You have now made one plait.
Repeat for all sections.

How To Cane Row

Comb out a row of hair.
Starting from front and working back,
Pick up three pieces of hair at start of the first row
And using a continued motion,
Cross hair right over left,
Picking up hair from behind the first bunches as
you plait along
Until you arrive at the back of the head.
You have now done one cane row.
Comb out a second row of hair.
Follow procedure above.
Repeat for all rows.

* * * * *

How To Begin Basic Dreadlocks

Wash your hair.
Leave to dry naturally.
Twist up your hair
Using the rope twist technique described earlier.
Over a month, continue to twist.
Your hair will begin to lock up.
As far as possible, keep your hair covered
Until the locks are fully formed.

How To Hot Comb Hair

Heat hot comb on a suitable appliance.
Test by placing heated comb on an old towel:
The comb should not singe the towel. If it does, it is too hot.
Add a dab of oil into the roots of the hair.
Section hair, from back to front, into rows
Then, starting at the back and working forwards,
Apply the hot comb to each section.
Repeat, working through all the sections.
It takes 7-10 hot comb reheats to do a complete head of hair.
Reheat comb for a final pass through the hair.
Hair will now lie flat.
Once it is straightened, add some oil to the hair:
This will provide a special sheen.

* * * * *

How To Recreate A Style of The Fifties

Conking
Conking was a popular Jamaican hairstyle for men in the 1950's.

Get hold of an Aloe Vera plant.
Cut it open.
Scoop the pulp out of it.
Leave the pulp to stand overnight.
By the morning it will have transformed into Aloe Vera gel.
In the evening, paste the Aloe Vera gel onto your hair.
Using a stocking end (or 'doo rag'),
Tie the hair down.
Leave the hair cover on overnight.
In the morning, hair should have the desired 'glossy ripples' or 'conking' effect.

* * * * *

Alternatively, for a laugh....

How To Cane Row

Find child
Get child and yourself comfortable
(Child's head should be at your hand height).
Have tools to hand:
Paddle: for slapping child if s/he starts fidgeting
Remote control: for TV control so you don't miss soaps
Telephone: friends' chat will make your hands fly faster
Shopping list: your useless partner can do shopping for once, you're busy, nuh?
Sweets: to pop in child's mouth before any fierce tugging.

* * * * *

How To Do Boys' Hairstyles Using Clippers

Discuss pattern requirement with the boy.
Explore all his preferences but
Veto all his rude, school-barred or crass choices.
Pause to allow his tantrum to finish.
Threaten to use clippers to pattern his head with a flower if he don't stop vexing.
Apply Playstation console to boy's hands
And plug in clippers.
(Get barber shop style Clippers and
Snap off all attachments even No 1)

Begin your design.
Show boy results in mirror
Threaten boy's father / older brother / siblings /
With poisoning if they don't say you done good
job on his hair to boy.
Sweep shavings from boy's neck with cloth.

* * * * *

How To Recreate The Styles of The Fifties

Get your oldest relative (with or without hair)
To show you photos of when they were younger.
Call man of house or oldest son into room.
Tell them to show respect and do they like
granpa's photos?
When they mumble, yes, scoop out the hotcomb
and Dax cream
From under cushion or behind mirror and
Tell them there is no finer tribute to granpa than
For them to don the hairstyle granpa had in his
prime.
Ask granpa to assist in pinning down reluctant
young male
Give said young male the old style haircut as per
the photo.

How To Do Extensions For A Friend

Bed down the baby, kiss kids goodnight.
Clear room of partners, worries, any sense of time
Sit down with good friend wanting extensions
Spend some time discussing which of the
Three extensions types she has brought along
Does she want to have on her head
And whose hair is looking good, whose not so good?
Make drinks. Continue this discussion.
...Oops you forgot what time it was?
You have not done any extensions
But you have had a great chat.
Cook good friend breakfast
And arrange another time for doing Extensions.
Repeat till good friend gives up and finds a salon.

Some Quotations

Grey hair is God's graffiti.
Bill Cosby

It's hard to have a bad hair day when you're famous.
Marion Jones

With hair, heels and attitude, honey, I am through the roof!
Ru Paul

If truth is beauty, how come no one has their hair done in a library?
Lily Tomlin

Life is an endless struggle full of frustrations and challenges, but eventually you find a hair stylist you like.
Author Unknown

Forget not that the earth delights to feel your bare feet and the winds long to play with your hair.
Kahlil Gibran

It is foolish to tear one's hair in grief, as though sorrow would be made less by baldness.
Cicero

He may have hair upon his chest but, sister, so has Lassie.
Cole Porter

A fine head of hair adds beauty to a good face, and terror to an ugly one.
Lycurgus

A celebrity is any well-known TV or movie star who looks like he spends more than two hours working on his hair.
Steve Martin

We lose our hair, our teeth! Our bloom, our ideals.
Samuel Beckett

Biographies

Rachel Van Den Bergen
Poetry springs into my head in bed, on the bus, walking down the street, anywhere. When it comes I have to write it. I'd like my poetry to connect me to people.

Trudy Blake
My poems come a little at a time, I put them together, they become whole: words that heal my sorrows, smooth away my pain, cheer me up, give me laughter instead of tears.

Debjani Chatterjee
I'm lucky to be living my childhood dream of becoming a writer. Writing is an obsessive joy and traditional tales are a constant inspiration. My first collection was *I Was That Woman* and recent books include *Namaskar, Masala* and *A Slice of Sheffield*. I also translate poetry from South Asian languages.

Tara Chatterjee
I always scribbled a bit, but after my husband died my daughter, Debjani, persuaded me to take up writing and translating. We translated a book together: Uma Prashad Mukherjee's *Album*. I usually write in Bengali and enjoy writing our family stories. Many, like my aunt Annapurna's story, are quite remarkable.

Julian Daniel
I am a Stand Up Comedian who also writes comic poems. So poetry is like a second language I picked up, I'm not sure where or necessarily why. As someone who's had dubious hairstyles in the past and will probably continue in the future, I decided to write Black Hair Day.
For more info www.juliandaniel.co.uk

Melanie Duncan
Poetry is my chosen tool of expression because it is a natural talent. Writing is a way to let the world know what is going on in my head. I believe that is why my novel is taking so long because I'm not yet ready to share so much of me but I can give you a taste through my poetry.

Jeanne Ellin
Poetry writing is a sudden gripping urge. I have written on a cheque lacking other paper! What I feel poetry is for is to surprise, move, even irritate but always to generate some reaction. Better a smack in the face with a wet fish than a mouthful of bland biscuit.

Rowena Fan
When I write, I normally have an image of the beginning and the end; the question is how I should travel from A to B. This was the case with *Childhood Hair*, which sprung as I observed my Nana's fragile

head, on her still-robust body. It is to her I dedicate this piece.

Jolivia Gaston

For a long time I've had a burning desire to write. Blackness is the main theme to my poetry, from childhood memories to bold statements. I want to explore worlds beyond the boundaries that society places on us. With honesty and faith I continue to write.

Asad-ullah Khan Ghalib (1797-1869: biography by Basir Kazmi)

Ghalib is the most popular poet in Urdu Literature, as well as being one of the greatest. His Persian verses too are of a high calibre. Mainly a ghazal poet, Ghalib extended the scope of this genre to such an extent that it became capable of expressing any thought or emotion. Ghalib's poetry is distinguished by his elevated thoughts, psychological insight and subtle treatment of themes related to almost every aspect of human life.

Khadijah Ibrahiim

I am the founder of *Sema Grass Roots* theatre production, where I develop and coordinate educational programs around social development for young people in schools and youth groups in the Yorkshire region. I am a poet, live artist, researcher and educator. I have been researching a larger poem on hair and *Bigwig n Suga Brown* is one extract from this.

Rashida Islam

I write poems, songs and children's stories in Bengali. My books include *Grandma's Treasure Trove*. Ideas come but I am careless about writing them down. This anthology's subject – hair – inspired me but writing my poem in English was very hard. I thank Debjani Chatterjee for editing my English.

G. Ovie Jobome

Writing to me is all about the story. The story kicks about in my head, and, when my brain finally kicks into gear, the story trickles out reluctantly via my fingers, and the keyboard.

Pete Kalu

I fall in love with some words and have a six month romance. Then we wise up to each other's faults. The fiction looks at me, jeering, 'you're not up to it'. I curse it back. Sometimes we make up, sometimes we go our own way.

Jackie Kay

Jackie Kay was born in Edinburgh, Scotland in 1961 to a Scottish mother and a Nigerian father. She was adopted by a white couple at birth and was brought up in Glasgow. The experience of being adopted by and growing up within a white family inspired her first collection of poetry, *The Adoption Papers* (1991). Her other poetry books are *Other Lovers* (1993), *Off Colour* (1998) and *Life Mask* (2005), all published by Bloodaxe. Her fiction titles include *Trumpet* and *Why Don't You Stop Telling Stories?* (both from Picador). She won the Somerset Maugham Award with *Other Lovers*, the Guardian Fiction Prize for *Trumpet*, and has twice won the Signal Poetry Award for her children's poetry.

Basir Sultan Kazmi

I was born with a poetic spoon in my mouth. When about four, looking up at some trees, I said, "Pappa, leaves!" According to my father, Nasir Kazmi, that was my first poem. I don't make an effort to write, but find that ghazals, other poems and also plays just insist on flowing out of my pen, as naturally as leaves appear on trees.

Nasir Kazmi (1925-1972: biography by Basir Kazmi)

Nasir Kazmi's elegant ghazals, filled with yearning and pathos, establish him as perhaps the greatest ghazal writer of the 20th century. The daily *News International, Lahore* recorded the generally held critical opinion that Nasir Kazmi had single-handedly revived the ghazal form and developed it into a modern and unique art-form. His lyrics transformed the traditional pessimism of the ghazal into an expression of the angst of modern man.

Shamshad Khan

I do a variety of things to try come up with poems for an anthology on hair. I sit and scratch my head for hairy experiences and anecdotes. I search out any existing poems with tenuous references to hair. I forget to comb my hair.

Sitara Khan

Having no idea of metre, I don't really regard myself as poet, but I'm told otherwise. Some pieces seem to take forever; others like the one in this anthology, come complete with every detail.

Usha Kishore

Poetry has always been a part of me. It has now possessed me and is wreaking havoc on my life. Some of my poems come out in full, others in dribs and drabs. I am an endless drafter; for this I blame the English teacher in me. *Moods of Hair* is an exile's journey into Indian culture, as is the rest of my poetry.

Chanje Kunda

I feel guilty when I don't write poetry, like I am neglecting someone I love. When I write I experience the thrill of conceiving something, bringing something to life. Poetry makes me feel worthwhile, like it's my time to shine. I dedicate my poems to my son, Nyah.

Segun Lee-French

I live parallel lives (((((Nigerian, Mancunian, singer, poet, producer/composer, playwright, linguist, film-maker, club promoter)))). One of the founders of Manchester's *Speakeasy People* poetry collective, I have won several awards for my writing for theatre & no awards for my poetry.

Jade Lloyd

poetry gives me space 2 explore n express emotions
poetry gives me a voice that is true 2 my experiences
poetry elevates my spirit flows naturally
now i know why the caged bird sings
Cause i feel a need 4 truth/s
dedicated 2 my beloved
Africa n fis.hy dreams
Living rhythm/s

John Lyons

John Lyons is a national award-winning painter and poet. He has four published collections, the latest being, *Voices From a Silk-Cotton Tree*, Smith

Doorstop Books. His poems for children and adults appear in numerous publications.

Buzzrak Mabrak
My influences are from the griot or public poetry tradition. My poetry connects with the political and social issues facing African Caribbean communities in the UK and beyond. I try to write with simplicity and engagement without shying away from complex subjects.

Sheree Mack
I'm a poet at heart. But I do write anything for money. I work well to deadlines and even set them myself. Tidying up, that's my thinking time. A very valuable time for mulling over ideas and words. Then, when I'm ready to write, its there.

Anjum Malik
Poetry comes to me from somewhere I cannot explain, like God, spirit, soul. It wakes me, stops me mid journeys, appears like magic, it's such a joy, always. I was born of Muslim Pakistani parents in Dharan, Saudi Arabia. I am also a scriptwriter for radio, tv, film and theatre.

Cheryl Martin
I started writing poems when I was nine. My brothers and sisters and I would make up stories

about undersea kingdoms and stitch pages together to make little books. A lot of my best stuff is about crazy things that happened in the family when we were kids – just change the names to protect the embarrassed. When I'm being good I start writing around six or seven in the morning, and I don't drink the night before. But when the deadlines come, it's all out the window – at the computer 20:7, skipping meals, living on crisps and cranberry juice. Not the best tactic – sometimes I have to re-write it. And re-write it. But sometimes – that's the one.

Shirley May

I love poetry and the opportunity it offers me to introduce my thoughts and rhymes to different audiences. I like to use poetry to look at personal, relationship and society issues. Most of my poems on the subject of Hair have come from a kind of meditation on my life, when I find the time away from being a busy mum and church woman!

Yvonne McCalla

As a little girl I'd get this itch in my hand, which required a pen and paper and ended up with me writing. Sometimes I don't even know what I'm going to write but when I get that itch I know something is on its way! Dedicated to my wonderful sisters, Yasmine, & Andrea.

Vijay Medtia

For novelists like myself who spend months and months writing a novel, the short story affords a small fountain of delight. A little gift that forms from varied experiences; sometimes an opening sentence leads to a short piece, sometimes a character or an idea. It is however always highly satisfying, and I sincerely hope the readers will enjoy it too.

Martin de Mello

I write both poetry and fiction. Being Eurasian and falling on the wrong side of many words the elusivene and resistant nature of narrative is of particular interest to me. For me the text is an audience in dialogue with the reader, offering ambiguity and endless possibilities.

Mir Taqi Mir (1722-1810: biography by Basir Kazmi)

Many regard Mir as the greatest Urdu poet. Equally loved by the educated classes and by ordinary people, he contributed immensely to the development of Urdu by transforming the language of everyday use into poetry. The ghazal was his main medium, though he also wrote in many other forms of poetry. Full of deep emotion and profound thoughts, Mir's poetry is generally considered the most effective expression of grief and a sense of loss.

Momin Khan Momin (1801-1852: biography by Basir Kazmi)

Famous primarily for his Urdu ghazals, Momin had a multi-faceted personality. He was a great scholar in Persian and Arabic, a renowned physician and an outstanding chess player. He was also well-versed in music, astronomy and astrology. Momin's poetry is marked by great flights of fancy, distinctive imagery, a particular Persianized style and the clever use of his nom de plume.

Dahu Mumagi

I enjoy trying to put some thoughts and feelings through the grinder, transforming them into a gooey paste and then moulding them into an intriguing shape. After this I like to bake them until well browned and serve them with a sprinkling of mystery.

Simon Murray

I write short stories, poetry, comedy and dabble in art. I once worked in advertising and am now writing a novel to redeem my soul. *Mi natty Dred don gimme Artritis* is a true story told by two of the many voices in my head.

Ghulam Hamdani Mushafi (1750-1824: biography by Basir Kazmi)

Like Mir, Mushafi was a prolific Urdu writer who composed in many poetic forms, eg ghazal, qasida (eulogy), masnavi (long narrative poem) and quatrains, but is best known for his ghazals. His works are available in nine volumes. A master craftsman who was emulated by many, Mushafi too is an important poet who continues to be read, enjoyed and appreciated.

Ahmed Mushtaq (biography by Basir Kazmi)

One of Pakistan's most important ghazal poets, Ahmed Mushtaq migrated to the USA in 1984. In his youth he wanted to become a painter or a classical singer, but he has said that his temperament and life-style did not suit him for the hard work necessitated by these art forms. As a poet, he likes to think in terms of sounds and images.

Deyika Nzeribe

Where does my poetry come from? I have no idea...I'm nearly 40, have bills, am discovering that middle age spread is not just a rumour, am still terrible at Japanese and my Rugrats have All Grown Up... It's turning me grey... I think there's a poem in there somewhere...

Elayne Ogbeta

In the beginning God created poetry. Let there be words - and there was! I love the way words mingle together, stretch your imagination, take you into another world and make you laugh! *Rapunzel, Rapunzel and HAIR* are dedicated to all those black women who appreciate the versatility of their hair!

Elaine Okoro

Writing has all the positives for me; it's where I feel I am worth something of value and importance. I come alive! re-connect to my spiritual self and others. Sometimes I get to use words like a sword on my don't-mess-with-me days. And officials and ex's have felt my words in their written form!

Pauline Omoboye

Through my verse come strands of memories. My hair has had at least one hundred hair styles. Inspiration comes from all corners. I dedicate my poems to my sister Mumba who brings new life, a future and more.

Kauser Parveen

I write to express unreleased anger which I have somehow contained over the years by continuous scribbles in an array of notebooks. I write about life, lifestyles, relationships and all that I witness around me. I dedicate all my work to the Mirza Family.

Eileen Pun

My hair poem is for my baby brother. When we were children we made names for the missing things; things that were not in the dictionary, slippery things that existed only in our imaginations. For the things that felt uncannily right, we named them *good feelings*. Poetry is my attempt to log those rare *good feelings*, and map my way back to experiencing them again.

Khadija Rehman

I find this style of writing easy because I'm a trained counsellor and also not forgetting to mention life's experience being my best teacher. When I come across any problem it appears difficult, but once I focus between the lines this then allows me to address the whole problem.

Desiree Reynolds

Very often I do so many things at once I can have an entire conversation with someone and not know what the hell they are talking about or what I've just said, at the same time as cooking mutton and rice and watching my boys, (I have two), be spiderman!

As for writing, well, I don't have time to write, or it's not given, I have to wrestle it from other parts of my life! I come from London, I live in Sheffield and after a long and windy road, I'm finally doing what I should be, in between the other stuff.

Alanna Rice

It started with a poem about a swan when I was seven and I'm still going. Subjects arrive without warning and I am moved to write. This, my first published poem, is dedicated to my grandfather - Neville Clarence Nightingale Esq. JP, and to my mother for keeping that first poem in her top drawer.

Tanya Chan Sam

Writing is something I love and hate simultaneously. It forces me to watch people and events, lets me see images and stories everywhere and makes me want to know more about the shred of idea I've had. I want my writing to keep me entertained for a long while.

Seni Seneviratne

There are so many stories from my childhood in the 1950's that I want to write. *Pipe Cleaner Perms* started as a poem but in the end it seemed more at home as prose. It's for my mother. She loved us in many ways and this is about one of them.

Kadija Sesay

I like telling tales within form and structure: like haikus and villanelles. I wish I had more time to write better poetry. Instead, I've become a nurturing anthology editor, loving mother to *SABLE LitMag* and a doting series editor for the *Inscribe* imprint of *Peepal Tree Press*.

John Siddique

Poetry crept up on me and mugged me, I was far

richer in a previous life, but without poetry I was a poorer man. Poems arrive usually at 4am, wake me up with their insistence, I find them running through me like a kind of music, and I just have to fit the words to that music. www.johnsiddique.co.uk for more.

Jackie Simpson

Poetry for me is an emotional expression of an experience that I have gone through or witnessed, before I put pen to paper. I write from my heart, leaving nothing out. Putting those emotions into words creates a picture in your mind. I dedicate *Natural High* to all my family, one love.

SuAndi

I try to capture a moment in time: a myth drawn from an actuality. I don't feel there is anything clever about my writing. Simple is what I achieve without even attempting to do so. I like to think the reader hears my voice and maybe in a quiet moment can recall the tale, the poem.

But I also guard the fact that as a Black poet I draw on ancestral tales told down the centuries by our griots and orators of history and to pen them anew. This action is sometimes subconscious. Sometimes it is the writing of intent, but always it is my stimulus and that enables myths and facts to lie together in verse.

Aissatou Sylla
I was born and raised in Gonesse, France. After surviving in London for three years, I moved to Manchester in 2003 and started writing poems with the encouragement of Commonword. A large part of my writing has evolved around my pitiful and failed attempts to have full control over my life, feelings, emotions or physical appearance.

Tina Tamsho-Thomas
I learned to write when I was three years old and cannot remember a time when I didn't pen poems. Writing is the most satisfying way of expressing my creativity, making sense of the world and problem solving. Black hair politics is one of many themes that inspire me.

Pev V'vshh
Words? Words are what's left of poems when the paper is gone.
Poems? Poems are what's left of life when the breath is done.
Life? A Life is what's left of belief when the be has been.
Go. Do. Be.

Kanta Walker
Writing a good poem for me is like waiting for the desert rain – there are long periods of vast, empty sand dunes with nowhere to hide and take shelter in.

After the rain everything transforms, flowers bloom, grass sings and life dons on a new enchanting coat every moment as it flows effortlessly.

Nyear Yaseen

Poetry is the voice in which I speak to an un-encountered audience; it allows me the veil of anonymity as well an insight into my perceptions of the environment around me. *My Hair* is my take on women whose hair tells you something about their inner psyche.

Nadeem Zafar

I guess poetry for me is very much a stream of consciousness type of thing. I write a lot from personal experience and on issues which affect us all. It is always spontaneous but it is never very difficult. In fact, the hardest thing for me is choosing the title. Once I have that, it virtually writes itself.